W9-AQX-381

PUBLISHER: Margaret Obank

EDITOR: Samuel Shimon

FRONT COVER PAINTING BY MANSOUR MANSOUR

CONTRIBUTING EDITORS
Fadhil al-Azzawi, Issa J Boullata, Peter Clark,
Raphael Cohen, Bassam Frangieh, Camilo Gómez-Rivas,
Marilyn Hacker, William M Hutchins, Imad Khachan,
Khaled Mattawa, Anton Shammas, Paul Starkey,
Mona Zaki

CONSULTING EDITORS
Etel Adnan, Roger Allen, Mohammed Bennis,
Isabella Camera d'Afflitto, Humphrey Davies,
Hartmut Fähndrich, Gamal al-Ghitani, Herbert Mason,
Hassan Najmi, Saif al-Rahbi, Naomi Shihab Nye,
Yasir Suleiman, Susannah Tarbush, Stephen Watts

EDITORIAL ASSISTANTS:
Maureen O'Rourke, Clare Roberts, Zoe Dexter,
Annamaria Bianco, André Naffis-Sahely

LAYOUT: Banipal Publishing

CONTACTS:
TEL: +44 (0)20 7832 1350
WEBSITE: www.banipal.co.uk
EDITOR: editor@banipal.co.uk
PUBLISHER: margaret@banipal.co.uk
INQUIRIES: info@banipal.co.uk
SUBSCRIPTIONS: subscribe@banipal.co.uk
ADDRESS: 1 Gough Square, London EC4A 3DE
PRINTED BY Short Run Press Ltd
Bittern Road, Sowton Ind. Est. EXETER EX2 7LW

Photographs not accredited have been donated,
photographers unknown.

BANIPAL, ISSN 1461-5363, is published three times a
year by Banipal Publishing, 1 Gough Square, London
EC4A 3DE

Banipal, founded in 1998, takes its
name from Ashurbanipal, last
great king of Assyria and patron of
the arts, whose outstanding
achievement was to assemble in
Nineveh, from all over his empire,
the first systematically organised
library in the ancient Middle East.
The thousands of clay tablets of
Sumerian, Babylonian and Assyr-
ian writings included the famous
Mesopotamian epics of the Creation, the Flood, and Gilgamesh,
many folk tales, fables, proverbs,
prayers and omen texts.
Source: *Encyclopaedia Britannica*

Nederlands
letterenfonds
dutch foundation
for literature

Supported using public funding by
ARTS COUNCIL
ENGLAND
LOTTERY FUNDED

www.banipal.co.uk

Mansour Mansour

Mohammed Khair-Eddine

Ghalya Al Said

Khaled Mattawa

Hussein Bin Hamza

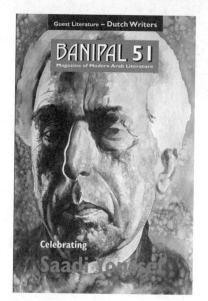

Guest Literature – Dutch Writers

BANIPAL 51
Magazine of Modern Arab Literature

Celebrating
Saadi Youssef

Jack Hirschman

Benjamin Burg

Franca Treur

Jan-Willem Anker

Aoe Tanami

Saadi, the internationalist

From the first issues of Banipal we have been proud to publish the work of Saadi Youssef in translation. Now he has reached his 80th year, we are doubly proud to present a special feature to celebrate his extraordinary achievements. In 1998, with Khaled Mattawa's brilliant translations, we published some of Saadi's poems from the 1970s, written in Algiers and in Baghdad, including "The Ends of the African North", "Endings" and "The New Baghdad". The poet merges his acute observations of daily life with his poetic heritage and vision to create, even in English translation, enthralling sounds and word-rich lines that cry out for performance. In 2000, we published the now internationally renowned poem "America, America", written in Damascus in 1995 when Iraqis were enduring hard years of US-led sanctions, again translated by Khaled Mattawa, who was to write later, in his book of Saadi's poems *Without an Alphabet, Without a Face*, that Saadi's "greatest contribution to contemporary Arabic poetry lies in his consistent effort to preserve the dignity of personal experience, despite and within a context of difficult sociopolitical realities in his native Iraq and in the Arab word at large".

In that same issue (*Banipal 7*) Saadi's great influence on other poets, and in particular Arab poets of the 1980s and 1990s, was clear to see. Abbas Beydoun described him as "a poet of universality and multiple open visions … he combines the physical with the metaphysical, the folklore with heroics, the epic with hymns, and the narrative with rhythm and Arabesque."

When I interviewed Saadi in 2004 (*Banipal 20;* online at *http://www.banipal.co.uk/selections/29/73/saadi-youssef/*) I learnt how hard Saadi had worked at being "free", having been forced to leave Iraq, spending time in Kuwait, and Algeria, then returning only to have to flee again,

to Tunisia, Morocco and Egypt, to Lebanon, Yemen and Cyprus, to France, to Syria, and finally to the UK. He explained: "I think of myself as a poet who is a resident of the world. I don't feel exiled. Being outside my country has become my ordinary life. I am used to it. I feel at home wherever I am. And I need to feel at home otherwise I cannot write poetry."

Saadi Youssef has the rare gift of being in tune with present-day life and being able to react poetically to everything going on around him. He is forthright and totally independent, speaking his mind in his poetic works, and shouldering the weight of Iraq's great heritage and suffering as well as attuning himself to an understanding of the legacies of imperialism. His life is in his pen, not a country, while the Arabic language is the means of his poetry living in the world as well as his translations of other poets and authors. In this feature there are new poems, written recently (all Saadi's poems are dated, you will notice), poems written for Saadi, tributes and essays, with some links to what is available online. Happy 80th, Saadi!

* * *

We start the last issue of 2014 with poems by the late Moroccan poet Mohammed Khaïr-Eddine, an unbeatable poetic wordsmith of the French language, and excerpts from novels by young Egyptian author Youssef Rakha, and Omani author Ghalya Al-Said. The Guest Literature feature this issue presents six very different Dutch writers, selected and introduced by Victor Schiferli of the Dutch Literature Foundation. Following our book review section, we complete the issue with a report and photos of Banipal's latest successful outreach event that took place last month in Japan.

MARGARET OBANK

MOHAMMED KHAÏR-EDDINE

Selected Poems

TRANSLATED BY GHADA MOURAD

DETERIORATED FAUNA

for S. Franco

They will come up to their image, in the muddy waters and under the trees; they will only see their eyes open on the ground, because they will fall as butterflies heavy with rain.

Thus begins another life from which all the paths of the world depart.

They glimpsed a bit of light and they said to themselves: this might be the day; but they never ceased wallowing in their blood.

Those who follow lines and never return,
those who wash in the azure their silhouette and stretch
out of themselves their arms to never grasp
go round in circles
and create a state of dizziness,
a fall;
these are the pure objects of our insufficiency.

Our ancestors were masters of solitudes; they ended life at the curve of a road. Centuries of men like bridge from tree to tree up to us.

My brothers call the common cycles; thus when the palms and the pack of winds conclude, begins the murmur of lips who proclaim you, O you who will lie naked on the beach; we shall find your beauty simple in the foam and the pebbles.

I lived in the redness of the stones that mark my plasma; I am the descendant of a forgotten race, but I bring in my hands the debris of their fire.

Our race will come, more immense than the fatal progenies. We see it when in a wing beat we tear each other up to shreds.

I have ceded to the impure and I have become a pond of microbes. Can I reduce their voracity, O, I already worn out?

I do not wish to be like the cicadas that heat had hollowed out. I am wearing a twilight and I invite the dead to decompose it. I live in the mud to listen to the rain turning me into a bee.

Many a holocaust came out of darkness; it returned, having taught anguish and destruction.

I speak to you, termites made of ice but in which the first quicklime is still burning, there is a mute desert that you fear, this same desert in you.

You create in proportion with the planets to fight the infinite; you commit suicide alone in your slow death; you raise thrones for your ingenuity, thrones of indignity; you're unaware that streams do not run below fatal attempts.

I do not surpass childhood (childhood for eachis a reference point), because it is no longer to resume a sequence of ideas badly cut out, ideas that bolt like thirsty mules, I do not even recall whether I made collages, I drew still lifes with the back of my tongue. It seems to me, however, that I had been language of a metallic country; nothing that comes from a finger. I was two opponents of a great quarrel, and if you understand me, you who believe in your body, you will repent. And you, tireless prospector, lover of the findings, stop and sleep in the sunny corpse of your reality.

I do not whisper any more, I am no longer present; horror of he who has been collapsing into himself, in the dust of the words that served to live. But survival might exist in the cosmic paste where the marsh has declined, an empty number of ecstasies which degenerate into gruff sounds.

I like to stay, the immovable sea still invents the road, the depth lived in phases of filth. And I will be sated from having thus endured; more male than carnal, I hold it, it vibrates; between the abyss and me is a reign and I am; splendor of which retakes the paths of a source.

I always move forward in the geometry of men,
through my fingers white wasps are slipping,
I collide at the simplest gesture of the earth,
a street arouses me and it is I who assume it.

Evening came, haze of soot on our faces, the city encrusted itself in the side of our history; my pores have known the blockade of caresses; somewhere the wind bit a desert and made the stars spring. Mine was a goat for having exaggerated the difficulties, and I wear it around my neck as an ultimate defeat.

Night runs in my skin, it screams: I am your real sweat. My temples can be read, see the high reliefs that relate many a battle: there was a portcullis that blocked the river, a richness stood between our faces, endlessly.

Another year has just come out of midnight as of an inexplicable crater, and yet no stone has moved. In time we go like tarantulas, we devour time with our mandibles. When our vague silhouettes are all that's left, we will consider.

The window was becoming deadly. It held me back. Men circulated. Gold in the abstract, from afar, blinded them.

In the morning, among thorns and fruits scraps, I found a wounded breast. Perhaps it is the world's.

The turtledove arouses many a fig tree, the eagle succumbs without having said his last word to the rock that raised him. There is another bird that haunts the torrent and that accuses him of having mumbled its waters.

The almond tree would be one of the few trees that can, in their silent whiteness nicknamed spring, hang death in the air; it gives the bare rock its purest music.

Where to break my legs bent under the weight of my blind brothers? I would like to offer him a death like the cry uttered by the child who discovers things: a strange phrase.

He had begun by dying; it was the exordium to silence, but unintelligible. He will receive the land and laugh innocently.

And of course men will attend his death. But I shall be the

only one to tear myself away from my body, as from a trap; I shall leave one wing.

And you, draw your dreams from their unanimous hands, ride on the river of men and dive and roll and twist and rebound. And you, bite, and you, smell, is there any other absolute?

To each one part, to the worm his. I shall melt; in the red snow of my carrion grass shall grow, day shall burst! new blackthorns shall lead the crusade to the most beautiful sands when in his beatings my heart shall sink.

Deteriorated fauna by dint of alphabet, here I am erected at the end of myself. All the lamps go out and I walk into the cave contiguous to my shadow, black diamond against which collide the insects that rise from the greenest of summer.

Translated from the author's *Faune Détériorée*, published by, Editions William Blake & Co. Art & Arts, 1st May 1997 in their "L'invention du lecteur" series of contemporary poetry and literary essays written in French, following its first publication in 1966 in the journal *Encres Vives*. http://www.editions-william-blake-and-co.com/
Faune Détériorée was one of the very first texts published by Mohammed Khaïr-Eddine on his arrival in France in 1966.

Four poems from
Soleil arachnide (Arachnid Sun)

MUTINIES

I need among other chances the sea
split as the woman born on the tip of vices
by the fornication of chiggers and yews

castaway
     how the novice act of my skin
arms by screaming sea the skins' red slumber

stamped by the stars' complex seal
I shake my sticks at the norms' blue face

nothing
    but a hiccup of fear chartered by the black adjacent
to your erected retinas of pagonies – a dead
sea of reticules – I close
the mould excluded from silence and your naphta
twirling

by the vicinal texture of the voices of the man walled
in the chaps of your orb
and the sun

split
        I laugh
    sea alight in the birds' unknown ink
by this scratch of given whispering sand
of satellites of eyes of meanders of midnights

I need among other chances this sea
split as a woman born on the tip of crimes
by the fornication of chiggers and vetches

DESCRIPTION OF A FLAG

to Mehdi Ben Barka

icterus of lamps cleaving the plasma of a dream
and the rain that prowls through me melted
in the sap right from the sky and the snow
disheveled by a god painted on my cramps
good heavens here they are naked and lapped my faith cries
    dreams
of the news item that uncoils the rectum of my land
strapped by the legs like the sacrificial steer
I strike out the oblique notebook of your rightness

MOHAMMED KHAÏR-EDDINE

and stilt a mint and thyme coffin
O land gradually found under the ancestral vice
vast cry when we climbed the white stone
with in our pockets the finest money of the air

gallop nine heads and
this nail bleeding in my eye

death is a tobacco leaf
you ruminate the morass death is a daring

gallop nine heads and
this nail trapping my eye

death is a kaleidoscope
where you question from your finger and navel
having embraced the shady oblivion of your litany
of birds buttoning asbestos
by days flames and by nights fires

O gallop how drunk of beating
on this morning of pangs supply
the bay of a memory that was not cherished

your face jailed already
the sun like an almond tree distraught
in the thrill of myriapods
and we were unique with all those
who saw a throne of insects decrease
flush with a hurrah of an island rising
in the bloods of a sea sizzling with joy

and now
death
thou you like a reed whose beetle says the force
of singing

icterus of lamps cleaving the known of a dream
disturbance fallen sun barbaric fabric of the post-reign

that we made red and signed
the star gazelle by that same day
by erysipelas of the desert where we sank

you die suddenly really you brandish your roots
in my unpredictable shadow where the men of Sakia-Hamra
moved gaze at you precipitate
on the chergui with which the Seine covered you

cellars
lengthwise
spiders' eggs perfuming the dictator silence
white murder on the edge of despair
the river Bou-Regreg says who crumbles you and where
your blood still laughs at the public enemy
revenge drying the throats
vermicular
of eyes of pebbles soaked in the boilers
of a life that closes on itself high and simple
to curse
no
to harpoon the king shark who then
left the riverbeds of polar bush
and chews his rancor with sometimes
like glass marbles that break
rubbish soot king
narrowness of the thought
of always riddling the flag with blood
with the song that runs in our viscera

SAGHO

the morning of blood sprinkled the sagas born of the scorias
of stars deflowered full blast
and raises my blood as a mustang beaten by eagles

from the high plateau where your fingers bend the sumacs fire

up to the steppe fractured by the eagles' beak
my questioning fists strike the sky

morning milk agrotis' and lily's salt
the abyss rewards us with the belly of an antelope shot in
the thunders' millet

but no word
no word if not the lyctus flour by this virile weather
and by sheaves the winds' aphids under the catnips

too bad if alone too bad I falsify the public sign
of dawn I rub my eye before entering the
inextricably clear custom of time

EXILE

We carry the old guns of the colonized
we accentuate the rage until we bend our faces
against the ardor of the nude against the arachnid sun
we carry the bomb we swing our torso
we distinguish the sawdust of our navels in the port
very badly borne from the old Portuguese kings DOWN!

stiff skin
skin
drums my fear jackal herd and wipes the snots of the dead
newly enrolled in my parricidal administration!

my flute gets involved and ends
the ambush through which your rebellion does not go
the dead island of my friend Césaire Hun according to Faye (is he
    wrong?)
autonomous vacuum according to the magazines and black
    musically captivated
by neurosis
according to
Sartre

O vitch! The friend from psychodermal metals!
huh! the forest dead ages
ago without cacophony THE SMALL METAPHYSICAL STUDENT ROOM!
I throw the ferns to the repressed marls I rant
I ignite Africa I arachnid I moth
my alcoholic snow and my cup
I find my skin under the decried sky I make
the black
intervene.

I turn on
plagues beautiful like your women
with depths charred with asthmas without star
I enter pygmy alone at the worst of stegomyias
where the sea spits out its blue song that a jackal
disembowels under the black spite of your udders

no
more dove!
she proliferates she is white she is
standing
I said
blood without bandoeng
atrociously argued this is the fife but when
then will this oil vine burst?
my violet language aims at it my isthmus language

we drag
the arachnids' childhood (MUTILATED)
country of exile cracked thirst old oaths
I protest She gives the wasps of the eerily beautiful
black bird-bitch when the weather triturates
the nuggets

Four poems selected from the author's collection *Soleil arachnide*,
presented by Jean-Paul Michel, published by Gallimard Poésie,
September 2009, 144pp, ISBN: 9782070359608
http://www.gallimard.fr/Catalogue/GALLIMARD/Poesie-
Gallimard/Soleil-arachnide

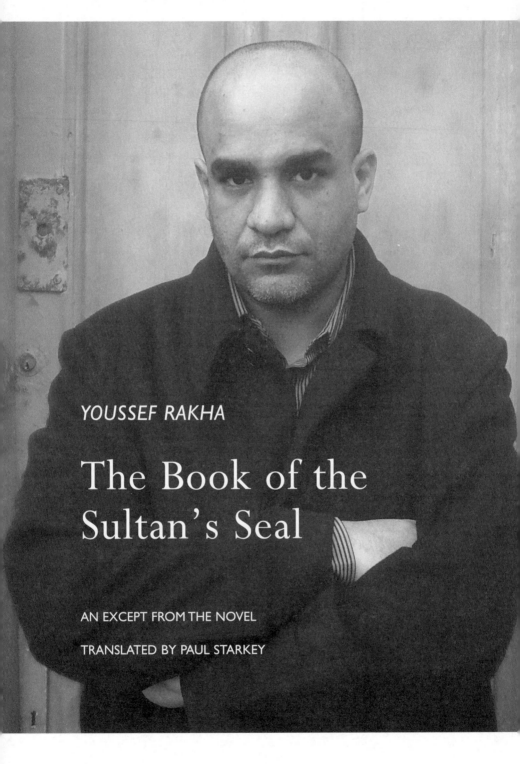

YOUSSEF RAKHA

The Book of the Sultan's Seal

AN EXCEPT FROM THE NOVEL

TRANSLATED BY PAUL STARKEY

On the Saturday evening, the first weekend since Mustafa had stopped at Dream Bridge, as he drove his Sunni friend to the Khan of Secrets, he became disturbed that the latter seemed determined to raise the subject of his separation. Amgad kept telling him that he felt that he—Mustafa—was egging him on to speak about himself, then not talking. He shouted in jest: "This is cheating, you're a cheat!" And Mustafa didn't know how to hide his anger.

They went back and forth about it through the entrance to the Dandy Mall. All the time Mustafa was doing his utmost to explain the problem in a way that Amgad could understand. He tried posing as reasons for the breakdown of the marriage anger, misery, conflicting temperaments. All this, only to discover that in the view of his retired policeman friend, he was simply repressing his wife. The problem, that is, lay in Mustafa's patriarchal authority.

"Oriental blood," he told him. "You just don't want to admit it."

"Admit what, Amgad?"

"And what's more, she was always kind of a hippie girl."

"She what?"

"She was always kind of a hippie girl," he repeated. "That must be why you suffocated her."

Mustafa started the TV peasant conversation again, to keep from getting worked up.

For more than a month, I'd been avoiding the friends who liked her, he said to himself: artists, poets, generally older than me. They could only see the glittering surface and the rising sun. I couldn't say to them: today there is nothing to keep me from leaving without negotiations. Did I lose those friends by avoiding them, only to end up with a donkey who thinks the problem was my patriarchal authority?

The light was shining in the towering arena of the supermarket, but the neon was like a whirlpool in the sea: nausea. Mustafa concentrated on their distance from the city. This was really why he'd come. After the collapse of the world, where could he go, except for the Khan of Secrets? "In the dictionary traveling means traversing distances. It doesn't matter if they're short or long, vertical or horizontal, on the surface or in the depths. To have experienced a journey you only need to have traversed a distance." He pulled Amgad by the arm across the entrance corridor. The groceries were piled high, as were the clothes. As usual, they headed for the electronics. Mustafa stopped without realizing it. He could just see Amgad eying the cookers. He drifted toward the microwaves and toasters on his own. He no longer moved in tandem with Mustafa as he used to, when Mustafa thought he must be afraid of being on his own. "My dubious journey, which always promises new stations and always costs me more tickets." Mustafa had only to straighten his head so as not to see Amgad. A face like his wife's flying past in the distance. Change and stability. A hot meal and a fuck. From where he was standing he looked at the cameras: silver, black, and metallic colors. Gardens of silicon, beneath which pixels flow. He stepped closer and stared. Lenses of different apertures, a photographer's bliss!

The big camera his wife had bought for him wasn't practical. If he was really going to move he'd need one of these. One the size of a packet of cigarettes.

To put in his pocket and fly.

* * *

"Where have you been, Mr. Çorbaci?" The pillar of bloated rubber was coming up to him.

"What?" he asked impatiently.

"Did you see that mixer, sir?"

ABOUT THE BOOK

Youssef Rakha's *The Book of the Sultan's Seal* [*Kitab al-Tughra*] was published less than two weeks after then Egyptian President Hosni Mubarak stepped down, following mass protests, in February 2011. Modelled on a medieval Arabic manuscript in the form of a letter addressed to the writer's friend, the novel is made up of nine Parts, each centered on a drive Mustafa Çorbaci takes around greater Cairo in the spring of 2007. These journeys create a portrait of Cairo, city of post-9/11 Islam. Meanwhile, in a series of dreams and visions, Mustafa Çorbaci encounters the spirit of the last Ottoman sultan and embarks on a mission the sultan assigns him. The book also includes sketches made by Mustafa, which illustrate his cartographic attempt to recapture a Cairo he feels he has lost completely. Brought together at the end of the book, these sketches combine to form the shape of the tughra, the seal of the Ottoman sultans.

Rakha's novel is a complex work, written in what the author sees as a new version

Delight on the pillar's face. He paid no attention to anything except kitchen gadgets.

Once again Mustafa left him and made for the DVDs. He needed a B-movie collection to fill the space in his room. The book selection proved limited and disappointing, as did the stationery. Amgad Salah was carrying two copies of a work by Sayyid Qutb, claiming that it was the "finest nectar." With some difficulty they found a place in the line. Shaving supplies and cans of juice. As they were packing their purchases into bags, Mustafa noticed that the light was gentler outside the supermarket—perhaps because the space belonged less to the Egyptian middle class than these rows of goods. With no people pushing and shoving like beasts, there was no reason for nausea, he thought.

From our own planet, outside the enormous square occupied by Carrefour, we can see Dandy Mall as a broad, twisting lane: keep walking and you'll return to where you began. But were the white walls really that dusty?

In Mustafa's memory everything is grey. But the sensation of travel comes back to him as his eye cuts through the fancy kiosks in the middle of the lane and settles on the rows of shop fronts on either side. You're walking on tiles, almost skating, relieved for a moment to be separated from everything. The asphalt and the red

of 'middle Arabic', and full of intertextual references to the medieval Arabic canon. It is both a suspenseful, erotic, riotous novel and an examination of the roots of the current Muslim predicament. Çorbaci's trials shed light on the contemporary Arab Muslim's desperation for a sense of identity; but the way to a renaissance, it is strongly implied, may well have less to do with dogma and jihad than with love poetry, calligraphy, and the cultural diversity and richness within Islam. Fantasy it may be, but this account of a man's 'sudden transformation during twenty-one days from a Europeanized intellectual to a semi-madman who believed he could perform magic deeds to resurrect the Islamic caliphate' (p.465) seems peculiarly relevant today. The extract here is taken from Part Three, "The Khan of Secrets".

PAUL STARKEY

• The Book of the Sultan's Seal: Strange Incidents from History in the City of Mars, translated by Paul Starkey, is published by Clockroot Books. ISBN 9781566569910, paperback, $19.95, November 2014.

bricks, the flies and the trees, the air, the exhaust fumes, and the sight of the sky. You adapt your walk too to a ceramic rhythm and feel that you're in a submerged airport where planes seldom land. Another reason to come to the Khan of Secrets? "Don't you miss flying, Sheikh Amgad?" Here was the sheikh jumping up and down with all his weight as he listed the merits of the mini-microwave that he'd made up his mind to buy.

In front of everyone?

And we forget his sorrows and his beard.

Mustafa jumped up and down with Amgad and was happy for no reason. Perhaps his happiness came from the fact that the place really was like an airport, in that you might be anywhere on earth. Then there was a light-skinned child so small that the microwave Amgad had decided to buy could hold all of him, no exaggeration. He was sticking his tongue out at Mustafa. His family seemed to have left him to do as he liked, and Mustafa couldn't see anyone with him, either in line or in the supermarket.

Now he was playing blind man's buff with Mustafa and laughing: sweet enough to eat!

* * *

Two steps forward for Mustafa to pretend to attack the child, and Amgad had suddenly disappeared. He must be somewhere between the Syrian sweet shop and the Costa window. But Mustafa had hardly spread his arms out when he stopped in his tracks. Ustaz Wahid al-Din, their zombie colleague, yes, flesh and blood, was pushing a large, empty shopping cart, the most striking aspect of which was that he was a long way from the shopping area. Outside the shopping area, you don't see shopping carts unless they are full of plastic bags on their way to the parking lot. Wahid al-Din was dragging his feet in his usual furtive way, walking with no obvious aim.

But as soon as he was opposite the young boy, he stopped and turned around. Suddenly, his movements became confident.

For the first time in his life Mustafa saw Wahid al-Din's back straighten and his face expand without embarrassment. He didn't doubt that Wahid al-Din was looking directly at him. His eyes were fixed on Mustafa's eyes without expression, and Mustafa was uncertain whether to say hello or to pretend to ignore him and look for Amgad. He also noticed that Wahid al-Din was wearing round old-fashioned glasses. For a moment, and this was the really surprising thing, he was certain he was looking at someone else who only resembled his colleague. Someone a little older, with a light beard instead of stubble. The agitated way he was moving had a certain gravity, so that rather than creeping along, he seemed to be exploring.

But it was suspicious, Mustafa thought, that this person was deliberately trying to give the impression of being Wahid al-Din. Why should this unknown stranger be deceiving me today? The unsteadiness at the two points where his lips met was more like sarcasm than anticipation. Who could Wahid al-Din's double in Dandy Mall be? Leaving aside his excellent posture, his steady stance, and the cheerfulness of his wrinkled face, the man's eyes were on him. And he was overwhelmed by a powerful sense that their meeting wasn't an accident. He was convinced that nothing in this world was an accident, in fact, but sometimes the feeling was so powerful that it hit you in the face. Like now.

When he asked himself whether he'd ever seen Wahid al-Din in glasses, he started thinking instead about what the appearance of his double here might mean, and about the possibility that it might have some connection with the Organization or the dream, or the prophecy—three things that were undoubtedly connected, though he had not the faintest idea of the secret that linked them. Suddenly, he came to, to find fingers like rubber burrowing into his shoulder, and discovered that without his noticing, the phantom with the out-of-place shopping trolley and the small boy in tow had disappeared. When Mustafa turned around, he blinked, because Amgad, who had just as suddenly reappeared, was holding something to his eye. He mustn't draw his attention to the presence of Wahid al-Din.

When he opened his eyes—he would continue to remember this moment—something that was a color between black and grey was moving away from his face, acquiring a faint sheen, and his Sunni friend's rugged voice was saying: "Have a look at this ring!"

Amgad jumped again when Mustafa tried to make out the engraving, which was large and blurred because it was still so near. Despite this (as would be explained by a visitor from another world, which Mustafa seemed to foresee), he could immediately make out its four constituent parts, and he let his mind wander over everything they suggested to him, still in a state of surprise from having seen Wahid al-Din.

Bagpipes

A boat

A water skin

A gazelle horn scabbard for a dagger.

For a moment, Mustafa thought that he might be looking at a map of the whole world in one engraving. This idea was reinforced by his realization that this was a decorative drawing of hard-to-read Arabic calligraphy (for some time, he had been taken with the idea that letters might depict a map). In the North there were three columns next to one another like a very thick flag pole. The curves emanating from them to the East came together in a tapered line like a sword. To the West there was an egg with its yolk, sitting on the trunk of a fishing boat in the South. The pole was joined to the trunk, and the sword emerged from the egg. Everything was connected by endless circles and arcs.

Later, after he had discovered everything and various preposterous things had happened to him, Mustafa would photograph the engraving on this ring with his large camera and reproduce it. It was shaped roughly like this:

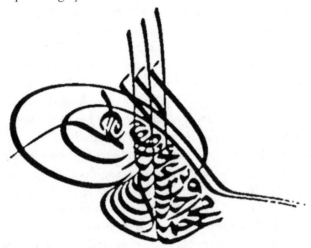

Without knowing it, he'd stretched out his hand to take from Amgad whatever it was Amgad was holding to his eye. At that moment the latter, his Herculean figure looming, noticed the scared look on his friend Çorbaci's face and asked him, in a slightly shaken voice: "What's the matter, sir, why are you shaking and that?"

"And what's up with you, Bashbushti?" replied Mustafa, trying to smile.

Only then did he realize that the engraving was very familiar. He must have seen it dozens of times, in names, trademarks, religious expressions, and even on a small coin bearing the words "Arab Republic of Egypt". But this was the first time he had made out all these allusions in it. From a distance, when he looked at it out of the corner of his eye, he noticed that it looked like a bird with an enormous comb and a hooked beak. For some unknown reason, without asking himself what it meant, he recalled the Qur'anic verse: "And every man—We have fastened to him his bird of omen upon his neck!"

But he quickly pulled himself together and resumed his conversation with Amgad.

"What is it that's written on this ring?"

"In the name of God, the merciful, the compassionate . . ." But as soon as Amgad had told Mustafa that, he began to have doubts. "Could it be something else?" Then he laughed shyly. "Look, I liked the look of it, that's all!"

"In the name of God, the merciful, the compassionate! What's that, Amgad?" sighed Mustafa with disgust. "You're making that up!"

They were quiet as they looked at the engraving. Most of the examples that Mustafa had seen really had had the expression "In the name of God, the merciful, the compassionate" on them, and sometimes "Muhammad, may God bless him and grant him peace." He didn't know what it was that had made him instinctively challenge Amgad's interpretation of the writing on the ring. But even odder was the fact that the ring actually bore another, completely different phrase, of which he could only make out the word "Ibn" ("Son of"), surrounded by circles of intersecting words.

"To be honest, I don't know what it says!" said Amgad as they stared at it. "But now I'm sure it's not 'In the name of God, the merciful, the compassionate'. Come on, why don't we go back to the shop to see what else they've got!"

And the other one nodded enthusiastically. "Did you buy it?"

"I could take it back, chief. I came to bring you for your opinion and that. I mean, I know that you love musk and the sweet customs of the Prophet . . ."

"Is the ring a custom as well?"

"But of course!"

Getting the Ring

The way to the silver window was longer than Mustafa had thought (there were intersecting paths with no logic to them in the Khan of Secrets), along a passage that branched off from the one leading to the restrooms. We say "window," because the shop as Mustafa recalled it was like a box of glass containing three silver shelves. It was surrounded by a square meter in which the salesman could walk about. Just a plastic chair, plus a calculator and a Visa card machine on the top of the box. No door and no windows. Mustafa looked up at the high ceiling. Everything was grey. There is a colorless detachedness to airports. The strange thing was that without thinking about it again he really did feel that he was in an airport. The walls were streamlined and sad. For another moment (though it seemed a very long time), as his gaze hovered between the ceiling and the walls, Mustafa remembered again what airports had meant in his life. The time when his father was working in Libya, his university years in southwest England on the coast of the "Manche" (or "Channel," as the English call it), then the search for his aunt the year she went on pilgrimage and didn't come back.

Between one place and another, there is always a dead time locked in buildings with colorless walls and high ceilings. He recalled that Plane Yard, like the Khan of Secrets in his current situation, promised an arrival that always remained at the stage of being fulfilled. Absolute time, or an eternal place. And there you seemed to be content to stay out of line.

In that absolute time, your compensation was the sense that you were moving away from the foundation pillars and blocks upon which your world was built—you had the sense, that is, that you no longer had a world. Nothing mattered as you followed your Sunni friend to that window. Amgad said, "Hey, sir!" and Mustafa looked in no particular direction. Amgad was asking the cheerful young silver seller whether the inscription said "Muhammad, may God bless him and grant him peace," while Mustafa stood two or three paces away, staring at the ceiling to shake the dust from his head. Very slowly he returned from his vision of Plane Yard to the conversation between them:

"This is basically Turkish script, sir!"

"Turkish, ah!"

"But naturally that doesn't stop you . . ."

"What do you mean, Turkish?"

"Turkish, sir, Turkish script. I mean, this writing is basically from Turkey or something. Of course, sir, that doesn't stop you from finding pieces with religious words written on them, 'In the name of whatever,' or 'Say, he is God, one,' things like that. But Turkish here, sir, isn't understood, because it's not Arabic at all, sir!"

"You mean, this isn't 'Muhammad, may God bless him and grant him peace'?"

"You could really call it Turkish calligraphy. Unfortunately, sir, this is the only piece I've got left. This shop is your home, sir, you can change it for something you like at any time. No offense, sir, I showed you a Throne Verse, something more than excellent, to be frank, but no offense, sir, you insisted on this one."

"Okay, what else could I exchange it for?"

"Turkish, sir, Turkish calligraphy."

Suddenly, something with four legs seemed to dart between Mustafa's shins. He started in fright.

"What's up, Mr. Çorbaci?"

"How should I know?"

Amgad smiled at the shopkeeper with the same self-confidence that had made going about with him change Mustafa's view of himself, before he'd become a Sunni. When he was dealing with shopkeepers and waiters, or even garage and parking attendants, he would take on the spirit of a kind and generous feudal gentleman. But why was the shopkeeper now suddenly grimacing and turning his face away from him?

His tone changed as he spoke to someone Mustafa couldn't see.

"Come here, boy!" he shouted.

Until he realized he was talking to the little thing that had made him jump. A glance to the left and he recognized his little white-skinned friend walking toward the shopkeeper with his head bowed. He was no taller than a couple of hand spans. As soon as the shopkeeper started talking to Amgad again, the child took advantage, and stuck out his tongue at Mustafa. Mustafa stepped forward, looked at the cheerful young man, and asked: "Your son?" This made the latter ignore Amgad a second time, and gesture with a mixture of pride and embarrassment.

Amgad was still hesitant as he examined the rings that the shop-keeper had brought out on a piece of dark-blue velvet. He turned them over in his coarse hands like someone tapping a watermelon to learn from the noise it made whether it was sweet.

"What do you think, Darsh? Should we take this one?"

Suddenly the whole of the Dandy Mall was flooded with Salah Abdullah's song from the film Soldiers in a Camp: "Hosta Kosta, high as a kite . . ."

"This Throne Verse is beautiful, Amgad," said Mustafa. "I'll take the Turkish one for myself."

"Sure?"

"Yes. I'll settle up with you. Just let me try it for size!"

As soon as he put the ring on his finger—as if it had been custom made for him—he was shaken by a new terror he could not explain. Just for a moment, during which Michel Fustuq's talk about him leaving the marital home and the church dream went through his head in turn. He was thinking about how the fair-skinned young boy had turned out to be the shopkeeper's son, which would ex-plain why he was wandering around the place alone. If I'd looked for him when he vanished, he wondered, would I have reached the window on my own? As it turned out, he'd come to the Khan of Secrets in order to obtain a ring, with an inscription that was at once familiar and obscure—perhaps the inscription had some con-nection with the events of the dream? Then there was the appear-ance of Wahid al-Din's double and the fact that his wife had been a bit of a hippie from the beginning. Without any question or answer, Mustafa knew that Amgad had this evening handed him his place in a battle from which he—Amgad—had withdrawn. He didn't know how, he just knew.

One last time he sneaked up on the child by and tickled him, be-fore leaving.

If anyone dismisses them or criticizes them, they call him an un-believer. Each of the heads of the group becomes a sheikh in his own right . . . judging, ordering and forbidding . . . (al-Jabarti).

It would've been better for them to walk around a little after put-ting their purchases in the cart, but Amgad immediately headed to the cake display window. Mustafa followed him slowly to the circle of light. The waiter there was more polite than was necessary. Once again, motion takes place as if in a dream, Mustafa frightened at the yellow light falling on Ahmad Salah's face. He just said to himself, the atmosphere is calmer than it should be. But he was apprehensive as they sat down. And indeed, hardly a minute had passed before the conversation turned to Amgad's persecution in the office, which is what he'd been dreading. An Arab soap opera whose episodes would never end. He recalled Amgad saying that they shouldn't talk to him like that, their colleagues. A sheikh with a beard and a prayer mark on his forehead—he said this without laughter or irony— should be treated with respect.

So far, he recalled, he hadn't succeeded in raising another subject. Even his separation was madmen's talk.

"Ustaz Amgad Pasha Salah!"

"Yes!"

"A beard without a mustache is a joke"—he couldn't believe that he'd succumbed to the explosion—"You don't look nice like that, not at all. And then, my friend, what's all this got to do with religion? The Prophet of God had a ponytail. I mean, if you mean to follow his example!" Then he shouted: "Piety isn't a mark on the forehead!" After which he hurried off, still shouting about the Day of Reckoning and the Resurrection.

He didn't come to himself until Ramses Square. Was he thinking about Yildiz all the way? It was better to avoid quarreling with Amgad Salah because he either immediately retreated or he hit you. He knew that Mustafa wasn't afraid of his blows. Still, the silence was absurd. Yet at least the subject was closed. He was no longer obliged to explain the basic meaning of the word Islam, nor his separation. At their next meeting Amgad would look for an opportunity for revenge. But for now, Mustafa was dropping him off outside his house as he did every time.

Amgad leaned through the car window to bid him farewell, looking around him like a hunted man. "As-salamu alaykum," he said.

And you, he was saying quietly to himself, are a laughingstock and a coward.

GHALYA AL SAID

Days in Heaven

AN EXCERPT FROM THE NOVEL,

TRANSLATED BY CHARIS BREDIN

London. Four in the morning. It was cold but rainless. A typical winter's night. Darkness had crept into every corner and the pale light of the streetlamps did little to dispel it. Everything was still, frozen in a deep coma. At this inhuman hour, all activity had ceased. Shops and restaurants had shut their doors, and even the swift, tireless motion of buses and trains had ground to a halt. In the deserted aftermath, the streets appeared longer and wider than usual. London was a city of ghosts.

Near Paddington Station – Praed Street to be exact – a single solitary figure was visible through the gloom, Ghassan al-Muntahi was draped in a long, black, woollen coat. His white shirt was open at the collar but he seemed not to notice the bitter cold biting at his face and chest. Only his lips – cracked, blue and numb from whisky – were starting to bother him. Black Label was his preferred poison and he had had his fill of it that evening.

Ghassan had lost much of the strength and vigour of his youth. His former energy had been worn down by the years and he now trudged unhurriedly along, a sad contrast to days gone by when he'd stepped proudly forward like an army on the march.

He was heading silently home to his small flat, tucked away on the top floor of a tall block. The flat was not actually his but had been provided by Social Services, through the Peabody Trust. Every week, Ghassan paid a small amount towards the rent, and the government provided the rest.

At that moment, Ghassan's head was filled with verse, for like the rest of the Forties generation he was something of an amateur poet. As usual, there was no one to hear his work, and so he diligently memorised every word and image lingering in his head, ready to scribble them down later in his special notebook. Eventually, he would record them onto a cassette tape – just in case he happened to meet a fellow poet one day, and wanted to display the rich words and dark sorrows conjured up by his 'genius', as he liked to call it.

Having already covered a considerable distance in his night-time wanderings, Ghassan was now minutes from the flat. He had set out from Westminster, the illustrious and refined end of town, the dreaming towers where laws and policies are first conceived. It was altogether different to where '. lived. Paddington was a noisy, bustling muddle of restaurants and cheap bars.

"How many adventures this flat has witnessed!" he murmured, drawing closer to his destination, "How many secrets it's kept from prying eyes! How many dark deeds it's concealed between its trusty walls!

"But perhaps it's not the building that's protected me. Perhaps it's the city." No sooner had Ghassan considered this intriguing thought than it occupied his entire mind, demanding immediate reflection. He resolved to find a response before he reached home, and if one were not forthcoming he would remain outside the flat, on the pavement, for as long as necessary. On closer reflection, however, he realised that the question was rather straightforward. It was clearly London that had kept his secrets. It was London where unquestioned social codes prevented people from poking their noses into other people's business. It was London where the individual's freedom was respected, and his secrets kept, so long as he respected the freedom and secrets of others.

This realisation immediately led to another train of thought, transporting Ghassan back to memories of misfortunes that had befallen his acquaintances in other, less permissive, parts of the world. Foremost among them was his Omani friend, Nasser. Some years ago, Nasser had become besotted with an older woman. The couple's love for one another grew so intense and all-consuming that they couldn't bear to be parted. Soon, they decided to live together in Nasser's house, and forever banish the pain of absence.

At first, no one seemed to notice their arrangement, but then, several days later, tongues began to wag. The neighbourhood women were curious to know who the lady was and soon a whirlwind of hypotheses was raging, with each lady having her own take on the situation.

Gradually, this state of bewildered intrigue intensified. It was, above all, the woman's advanced age that had outraged people so.

"What can that woman possibly be up to in the house of a young bachelor like him?" they whispered to one another. The couple paid no heed to the gossip and inquisitive glances directed their way. Then the Muezzin, one of the neighbourhood's more prominent members, decided to wade in, bent on ascertaining the nature of the couple's relationship and, more importantly, whether their co-habitation could be considered legitimate when the young man remained a bachelor. He strongly suspected that there was some dark business afoot.

Tales of the woman spread like wildfire. She was the talk of every social gathering, particularly the women's coffee hour, which was not merely dedicated to consumption of dates and coffee, but rather, crucially, was an opportunity to have a gossip. Indeed, the women had no qualms about delving into the sordid secrets of people's lives, even when such matters did not concern them in the slightest.

Eventually, the Muezzin decided to raise the issue to the judge, feeling it incumbent upon him as a responsible and senior member of the community with personal ties to the mosque. He requested that the judge investigate Nasser's story and establish how this woman – Salamah – came to be in his flat. Why was she living with a man who was not her husband? She must be cautioned. She must be reminded that the customs of their country did not permit her to live with this man. The judge had no option but to call Nasser and Salamah before him and demand that they explain themselves.

In response to the judge's interrogation, Nasser simply stated that Salamah was renting a room from him. As he was struggling financially, he'd seen nothing against it. Thus, their relationship was no more than that of landlord and tenant.

On hearing this, the judge deemed the matter closed and cleared them of all charges. But the Muezzin, still not satisfied, raised the case to a higher court.

Ghassan let out a short laugh, replaying the story in his mind.

"That kind of thing would never make it before a judge in London," he mused, shaking his head, "for starters, there're no Muezzins. The neighbours wouldn't bat an eyelid either. Ever since

I came here in 1970, no one's ever tried to stick their nose into my business. My secrets have stayed firmly nestled between these four walls, completely safe from scrutiny. I've been left entirely to my own devices, without even making an effort."

Ghassan's many shameful misdeeds had, as yet, gone undetected. He'd carried out all sorts of sham deals and petty thefts, bullied his elderly wife constantly and told an endless string of fibs, luring gullible women into his trap then taking off with everything they owned. For the past thirty years, he'd led a double life, split between an acceptable public façade and a secret inner world. His wife Clara had some idea of his duplicitous existence, but only after years of marriage.

"I would never have got away with it back home, with all those suffocating traditions," Ghassan sighed, "I'd have been uncovered sooner or later. Perhaps I could've kept up pretences for a little, but soon I'd be at the centre of some scandal or other. A social outcast with nowhere to go. All my thefts and scams would've been found out. But secrets are secrets in London. Unless you're one of the Rolling Stones. Or Rod Stewart. Or Princess Di. Or that writer Fay Weldon. Or Joan Collins, for that matter. When it comes to their like, there's no such thing as a private life. There are people who are experts in digging up their own dirt.

"In London it's been a breeze. I've become a whole new me: a handsome, comely gentleman, with fine leather shoes, a sharp suit, gold wristwatch, and bulging wallet.

"No one knows the bitter reality behind all that: a life filled with every kind of failure. I'm a dropout. Bunked school, abandoned university, and never held down a job. I let things slip and ended up in a deep pit of vice that I've never managed to escape.

"Every morning, when I go to wash my face after a long night of drunken lies and debauchery, I peer into the mirror and all I see is bitter failure etched across my features.

"But no one's ever found me out, even as I walk towards the police car at the bottom of my building. Maybe if somebody had, I would've regained my senses. Perhaps the very fact that my other side has remained concealed for so long has reinforced it, pushing me further down this path. London's brought out a whole new side in me. I'm on benefits and I've no right to be. I've surrounded myself with a wall of lies that could quite easily come crumbling down, exposing my sordid life for all to see. Suddenly they'd all know I'm not Issam al-Kabir but Ghassan al-Muntahi, an uncouth, penniless, two-faced fraud, with a fake degree to boot."

As he continued down the street, his head buzzing with these thoughts, he suddenly realised that he'd already spent his entire weekly allowance and had not a penny to his name. At the same time, his thoughts drifted to his most recent girlfriend who knew nothing of his secret life, and, above all, the fact that he had an old wife called Clara and lived with her in a poky little flat.

Whenever his girlfriend raised the subject of marriage, Ghassan would prevaricate, hinting at the idea but never going further. He was a married man, after all, and could not possibly take another wife! At this, he was comforted by the fact that, in spite of the general messiness of his life, he did possess some commendable traits. He'd produced some decent poetry, after all, and dabbled in journalism many years ago. In fact, his passport even gave it as his profession.

Having left Big Ben and the Houses of Parliament far behind him, his building was now visible, shrouded in darkness, its large windows overlooking a dingy alleyway where mice and foxes were at play with alley cats and stray dogs. His head was still ringing with half-thoughts. He recalled the day he'd left home under a cloud of shame, his name linked to all manner of crimes, shunned by both his family and countrymen.

London had seemed the best place for developing his new persona. No one would ever know about his shameful past, and his family would never discover his new home, or the vice-ridden, lawless life he lived there, many miles away. Thus, he'd lost all contact with his former life, dropping friends and family alike. For all they knew, he could be long dead.

He'd come to London and lost himself amidst its thronging masses, living a covert existence, just like the millions of other wretched beings who'd sought refuge in the sprawling metropolis. Lost in thought, Ghassan had now failed to realise that he was metres from the flat. Before he reached the door, however, a new poem popped into his head, celebrating the passionately quarrelsome night he'd spent with his girlfriend until the wee hours of the morning. Her name was Kadi and she was very short, a trait he found particularly alluring. Ghassan always went for unattractive women, fat enough to inspire only pity and disgust. This was not a random predilection, but a deliberate choice. In his eyes, it was a very wise policy, allowing him to lessen his own sense of shortcomings.

Ghssan never fell in love with women either. Despite his passion for music and poetry, he simply didn't believe in romance. When it came to the opposite sex, all he knew was how to bully and domineer. In his view, women must be entirely submissive, with no voice or opinions of their own.

Instinctively, he'd realised that any woman with the slightest degree of beauty or intelligence would never accept him. Beauty, intelligence and independence would all inevitably become weapons levelled against him.

Reviewing the past evening with Kadi, he mused over how she and her friends always paid special attention to him when he was the only male present, amidst a crowd of ten or so women. Nights like that always filled him with an overwhelming sense of wellbeing.

Such soirées were usually devoted to him telling the girls weird and wonderful stories, in which he always starred as the courageous hero. In his latest tale, he'd described how he'd rescued a group of girls from the police, just as they were about to be handed over to immigration. Thanks to his close acquaintance with the Secretary of State for Immigration and Passports, he'd secured their release. Several members of the audience were rather sceptical of Ghassan's tale but did not press the matter, for fear of wounding his pride. They let him weave his fabulous stories and flaunt his exceptional and multifaceted talents, an activity that provided him with great psychological support, allowing him to gloss over the insecurities and anxieties that constantly hounded him.

Finally, he reached the small red door to his flat and inserted his key into the lock. He hesitated for a second on the threshold, uncertain whether to head for the bedroom on his right, or the sitting room on his left.

After a brief moment of indecision, he went for the bedroom where his sleeping wife lay in an exhausted heap on the rusty iron bed.

"Worn out after a stressful day at work," Ghassan muttered, gazing down at her, "and when she gets home, I just make everything worse by picking fights. I'm such a perverse guy," he shook his head, still observing Clara, deeply asleep and entirely unaware of the thoughts going through her husband's head. "Shall I jump in bed and have a go at her? She's my lawful wife, after all. My lawful wife, whom I've submitted to so many humiliations over the years. Look at her! Completely defeated! She's relinquished her whole being to me. All that's left is the shell of a woman, nervous and submissive, her back bent by the years and aspiring to no more than her miserable existence with me. Even if she wanted, she couldn't change it.

"I've a desperate urge to yell in her ear and wake her up. It's her to duty to wake up because I'm her husband. What a wretched woman she is: an old wretched woman who had the bad luck to cross paths with me. If Clara had any strength of character I wouldn't have lasted a day. I only ever pick weak women. That's why I've ended up with an ugly, old wife and an equally ugly girl-friend. And no matter what mischief I get up to, Clara will never leave me."

As these thoughts continued to swirl through Ghassan's head, his eyes wandered over the small, tidy bedroom, dimly visible through the darkness. He still hadn't decided whether to launch himself on Clara or turn the light on so she'd be startled into wakefulness, ready to brew him a cup of coffee that would hopefully settle his drunken mind.

Then another thought occurred to him: he could return to the sitting room and neglect Clara completely. This was his usual course of action for he found that the more he neglected her, the more de-voted Clara grew, striving to please him in every possible way, desperate for the slightest gesture of affection and terrified by the thought of him leaving her. The worse he treated her, the tighter she clung. Ghassan thus withheld all tenderness and grew ever more intent on demeaning her, making absolutely certain she stayed with him. Without such precautions she'd certainly have rebelled by now, abandoning him when he needed her most. He couldn't live in London without her. He was certain of that fact and dreaded the day when she finally kicked him out. Where would he go? What would he do?

He couldn't bear the thought of losing her and in his view this was a perfect reason for abusing and harassing her. Constant humil-iation was necessary to ensure that his word remained law. He simply had no choice.

For now, Clara remained firmly under his thumb. When they sat together in the living room, Ghassan would take the sofa, his long legs resting on Clara's lap as she perched on a small, battered blue chair, literally cowering beneath his boots. It was Ghassan who then chose the channel on the rickety TV set, loaned from Radio Rentals for five quid a month. Clara paid the fee out of her wage but it was he who dictated what they watched, never once consulting her. It was as though he were alone in the room, while she sat in stupefied silence, mesmerised by the images flashing across the screen and never thinking to challenge his assumed monopoly.

During their evenings in, Ghassan would always receive an incessant string of phone calls and Clara knew it must be "that short girl", with fat lips and big breasts. Ghassan had met Kadi two years ago and they continued to date. Clara knew that Kadi had no idea about her and the fact that she had been living with Ghassan for so long. Ghassan continued to hint at a proposal, with the result that Kadi called him ceaselessly, day and night. Clara would listen to their flirtatious conversations, her insides burning, her heart pounding and her nerves jangling. She never said a word though. She let Ghassan continue to his heart's content, hoping only that, one day, a small portion of his affectionate flirtation might be reserved for her. This longed-for attention was not forthcoming, however, so she reluctantly continued to battle her anxieties and jealousy, accepting everything that came her way. Inside, she was filled with hurt and a crippling fear that, if ever she contradicted him, Ghassan would leave her and fall forever into Kadi's clutches.

There was no doubt that Ghassan's relationship with Kadi had its benefits too. Each week, he spent a quarter of the girl's wages on cigarettes, coffee and wine, considerably reducing the hefty expenses that had previously been lumped on Clara alone. Ghassan's contribution to the household mainly consisted in doing their weekly shopping.

As drunken thoughts cascaded through his intoxicated brain, Ghassan still had not decided whether to launch an attack on the sleeping Clara. Perhaps he should leave her until the morning when she would begin hunting for him, as she did every day when she awoke to find him absent from her side. She would storm angrily through the flat, peering into every corner as the image of Kadi danced before her eyes. Then she would start screeching at the top of her voice, heedless of the neighbours and the disturbance she might be causing them so early in the morning. She shrieked mindlessly, entirely absorbed in the sound of his name: "Ghassan . . . Ghassan . . . Where are you, you bastard? Where've you got to? Where were you last night? Were you with her, that empty-headed bitch? Tell me! Were you in her arms? What does that hussy give you that I don't? Don't you get enough love and affection at home? Why do you insist on betraying our love? Or is it just sex? Is that why you like her so much? Don't you get enough of that here? Aren't I up for it day and night? I'm prettier than her as well!" Here, she would pause for breath, gesturing towards her face: "Just look at my plump cheeks, glowing skin and bright eyes. She doesn't have any of that . . ." Trailing off, she would then begin to weep.

When she eventually located him, her anger would subside and she'd slump onto her chair. A few moments later, it would dawn on her that she'd just woken up and hadn't yet washed the stale smell of sleep and cigarettes from her mouth. Nor had she put her false teeth in. She was a mess, without a speck of mascara around her tired eyes. Overcome with embarrassment, she'd hurry to the bathroom to sort herself out. It was of paramount importance to her that Ghassan saw her as a dreamy, fresh-faced girl, although, deep down, she knew she'd only ever be an old crone in his eyes.

Over the years, Ghassan had developed certain methods of forestalling her habitual morning tantrums. He would, for example, remain seated in the sitting-room, pretending to have been home all night, reading poetry, sipping wine and watching TV until morning. He would act cool, despite the fact he was quaking inside, and eventually emerge the victor. What terrified Ghassan the most was the fact that Clara was a woman with rights. Although not English, her residence in the country guaranteed her all the same protections as British women.

There was nothing to be done about these British laws and they were a source of constant anxiety and annoyance to Ghassan. He knew that if he went too far, bullying and tormenting Clara with his affairs, she might eventually go to the authorities. Then he'd be kicked out and end up on the streets. That was to be avoided at all costs.

Their flat was the one thing that was actually his, apart from a carton of cigarettes and some clothes. There were also a couple of gold bracelets and some electrical devices – all stolen – but they were going to be pawned at one of the local shops to pay off his debts.

Sitting quietly in the living room, he surveyed the furniture he'd never paid for. Some of it had been given by former lovers and some of it was stolen. A clutter of random objects filled the rest of the space: clothes, abandoned papers, cassette tapes, cheap nick-knacks, mementoes and knockoffs of Constable, da Vinci, Picasso and Rembrandt, bought from sellers in Hyde Park.

Ghassan remained where he was, waiting for Clara to enter and thinking bitterly of the laws that gave her so much power over him. He inwardly cursed Britain and its modern legal system that granted women so much more than they ever granted him in the way of social, financial and intellectual support. In his view, their rights should be immediately revoked and given to men instead.

Back home, women couldn't even travel without the prior consent of their husbands or guardians. In his opinion, this law protected both the family and the society as a whole. It had nothing to do with disempowering women, as was the general consensus in Europe. British law simply stripped men of their rights in the name of protecting women. The discrepancies in the legal system made his head spin. He simply couldn't make head or tail of them.

During all this, Clara was in the bathroom, attending to her morning cleansing ritual. As she did so, a question popped into her head: "Where was Ghassan all last night?"

No sooner had this question occurred to her than she barged through the bathroom door with a face like thunder, stomping over to him with a shoe in one hand. She immediately began to beat him viciously over the head and chest as he howled with rage, trying to escape the blows raining mercilessly down on him. She was humiliating him, emasculating him with every pound.

"Darling! Please stop! I never left the flat yesterday, you've got to believe me!" he pleaded, and she finally relented. "I've been on the sofa all this time, watching telly, writing poetry and finishing the wine I brought back from the restaurant. That's the truth! I did talk to Kadi but only for a little, and only to convince her not to call me anymore because I can't marry her. I made the situation quite clear to her. I promise!

"I told her I'm going to leave London for good and she can't stay on her own any more. But let's be honest, Clara," he continued, alerting his wife to an important point she seemed to have over-looked. "It's in neither of our interests to force Kadi from our lives. She provides us with valuable financial support, as you well know."

Clara's eyes widened at the words "financial support" for this had indeed slipped her mind as she raged against him. She really didn't want to lose the extra income and go back to bearing the full brunt of Ghassan's expenditure.

Some time ago, the couple had reached an agreement, with Clara consenting to her husband's affairs so long as they remained casual, and brought some kind of material benefits.

At the time, Clara had agreed reluctantly, and, as she feared, the moment had indeed marked the beginning of a long string of infi-delities, eventually becoming one of the mainstays of their marriage. Ghassan's liaisons were now a given that could not be questioned, so long as Clara wished to remain his wife.

Excerpted from the author's novel *Ayam fil-Jannah* (Days in Heaven) published by Riad El Rayyes, Beirut 2005

Celebrating
Saadi Youssef

Saadi Youssef started writing poetry at the age of eleven and has never stopped. Born in Basra, in 1934, in the same area as Badr Shakir al-Sayyab, Saadi was twice exiled from Iraq, and lived in many countries before settling in the UK in the late 1990s. As well as writing poetry, he has translated major international poets from English into Arabic, including Walt Whitman, C P Cavafy, Yannis Ritsos, Federico Garcia Lorca, Vasco Popa and Giuseppe Ungaretti, as well as novels by Ngugi wa Thiongo, Wole Soyinka, Nourridine Farah, George Orwell, David Malouf and V S Naipaul.

Saadi Youssef has lived more than half his life outside Iraq, but rejects the label of exile in favour of resident of the world, which allows him the independence of mind he requires for writing freely. Since the mid-1970s he has been, and still is, hugely influential among younger generations of Arab poets through his way of writing, and as a man with a life-long commitment to justice and human rights. As Hussein bin Hamza writes below, "poets of subsequent generations have found in Saadi's poetry a sounding board for their experiments".

Important works in English include Saadi Youssef's first major English collection *Without an Alphabet, Without a Face*, translated and introduced by Khaled Mattawa, and published in 2002 by Graywolf Press; Yair Huri's *The Poetry of Sa'di Yusuf: Between Poetry and Exile*, published in 2006; and *Nostalgia, My Enemy*, translated by Sinan Antoon and Peter Money in 2012 (Graywolf Press). Saadi Youssef has published, in Arabic, more than thirty collections of poetry, a volume of short stories, two novels and several essays. His Collected Poetical Works spanning 62 years of poetic output were published in June 2014 by Manshurat al-Jamal in Beirut in a 7-volume set.

• Readers will notice that in this feature there are different transliterations of Saadi's name, according to different linguistic styles and customs.

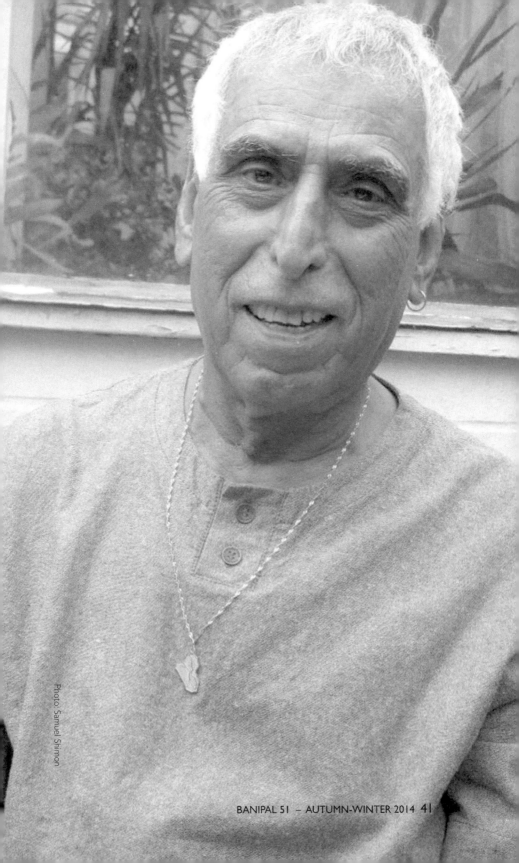

SAADI YOUSSEF

Selected Poems

TRANSLATED BY KHALED MATTAWA

AN ATTEMPT AT UNION

I told myself, why not spend the day (a silly ritual) walking
    around the duck pond.
Then I wondered: What's the sense of going there?
The ducks, so called, do not suit me, and the water running
    there is not my water.
The trees (stripped naked by autumn),
do I suspect them of being date palms?
And this bird?
If it winged toward Baghdad it would be hunted and eaten . . .
And these women guarding the park, if they moved to Al-Rashid
    with their dogs, they'd be nothing more than hostages . . .
Woe is me!
Now,
I felt embarrassed
by my state of mind . . .
A young woman with a dog that looked like a bird passed by:
Good morning!
Then *Sabahul-khair,*
I greet her
in Arabic!
The bird-like dog welcomes me saying:
Sabahul-khair!
Good morning!

But the girl, tall and proud, dragging her dog
did not bother to return my greeting . . .
did not care that the dog, in his fashion, continued to greet me . . .
. . . .

....
....
What a silly ritual!

London, 19.11.2011

A QUATRAIN

Ash clouds cover the hilltops,
the lake almost frozen,
and the birds are gone.

We'll go to the village pub in the afternoon.
The beer is cooling
and the curtains are burdened with haze.

The church, as always, is on the foot of the mountain.
And on the square the soldiers are dead,
the tower a nest for crows.

An evening without anguish, or candles commemorating
another evening, and no songs,
                     an evening that tosses me
into a waterless desert where devastation lies.

London, 20.12.2011

A SUNNY DAY IN MONTMARTRE

You will climb slowly to reach the square.
People have remained,
centuries
biding their time, rising to Montmartre
like pilgrims
of old.
The streets are paved with stones,
and Montmartre is paved with paper.

I asked about old friends who lived here,
who painted
to earn
their bread
and a bit of cheese to chew on and some wine.
Not one of them is here.
They left.
They all left . . .
To where?
Montmartre is packed, and paved with paper
and the streets,
same as yesterday, are paved with stones.
The ones you knew
have left
and grayed,
and melted from grief.
Do not be dismayed
and do not say
goodbye to the streets, even if they disown you.
The streets are your mother.
They suckled you
on the madness
of life's parade

*
Let's celebrate!

London, December 22, 2011

MOON IN ENGLISH WINTER

Moon,
a dagger made of copper,
a crescent broken by the night woods.
No star.
Moon in the rheumy eyes of English winter,
despised,
withered,

inert.
No eyes pursue it,
no songs praise it.
A moon not for poets
(You can see them all in their pubs),
or for young women
(drunk and stumbling in exotic rooms).
Nothing remains but the moon . . .
alone in the maze
. . . .
. . . .
. . . .
But someone, a thin shadow,
stands now, trapped in the night.
He opens a window
and stands a while
and goes on standing
until the moon disappears.

                    London, 28.12.2011

WOODPECKER

The woodpecker did not visit at New Year's, as he used to,
and as I have come to expect
the great tree has remained naked, ready, waiting,
but the woodpecker is late,
did not come at New Year's.
It's as if the woodpecker felt that I needed to ask him something
(Do woodpeckers foresee?).
But if the woodpecker had come to the village today
and planted his chisel beak in the trunk
and began to tap
and tap
I would have said to him,
"Give me, O dear visiting Woodpecker,
give me your beak, a few minutes,
a few minutes, that's all!

Give me your beak
to jab the Cyclops' eye
and flee my prison!

London, 04.01.2012

EVENING BY THE HARBOR

Three gulls dart,
whirling around hotel antennas
then speeding off toward the sea.
The evening saunters on the roads,
in the steps of girls
and cart vendors . . .
But night will come even to this poor neighborhood.
Night will come . . .
and the girls' steps will drift away
and the vendors' carts.
. . . .
. . . .
. . . .
Three gulls speed away.
Where do you think they'll sleep?

Tangier, 24.01.2012

HOUSE

I am looking for a house.
For years I've been looking for a house.
How many countries have I roamed looking for a house?
How many continents!
How many women's dresses?
How many killing fields!
And how many books . . .
how many cities!
Finally:

I am in Tangier looking for a house
and for years in Tangier I've been looking for a house!
But I'll return (as I was) without a house.
The no-house is my home then. So it seems!

Tangier, 07.02.2012

FOG

No boats loom on the river
and the scattered trees hide behind a sky-wide sheet of cotton.
Only the fence rises black among the white.
The birds that chirped in the early morning fall silent
and the light fades around the glass lanterns.
The green of the grass darkens too.
The doves will not come.
The thicket has closed its doors
and disappeared
in the fog.

London, 02.03.2012

IRISH SAINT

Ireland's patron saint,
St. Patrick,
today you see him in pubs:
Cabbage and ham and Irish dark beer overflowing
(For free!).
Usually, I head to the pub on his day
for the cabbage and the ham
and the free beer too . . .
But not today.
I did not go because I was on my own:
I did not have a lady to help me with the burden of feasting on
    cabbage and ham…
Was I wretched?

Maybe,
but not because I did not make it to the pub . . .

London, 17.03.2012

The above poems are from the poet's collection
Tayaran al-Hida'a (The Flights of Buzzards)

THE TELEPHONE IS CHOKING

She was moaning . . .
Her voice through the hoarse phone was choking.
At the edge of the garden,
the old chestnut casts her yellow shade
And in the olive sapling by my door, buds are greening,
their tips blazing yellow green like olives . . .
Her voice was choked:
I love you!
How did you leave the city, rambling at dawn?
How did you know how to find the station?
There are no taxis here at dawn,
no horse carts,
no boats yet on the canals . . .
How did you reach London all hung over with wine before I
    awoke?
I love you!
You are always like this . . .
I love you!
You are always like this . . .
. . . .
. . . .
. . . .

Do you remember the old bar in Paris, the trucks there
and their scoundrel drivers?
Didn't you leave suddenly then, just like today?
But I love you.
You are always like this . . .

London, 30.04.2012

PATIENCE WINS THE RACE . . .

To reach Octavia's flat
means climbing her narrow wooden stairway
like stairs we learned about on cargo ships . . .
And it means enduring a face-off
with her dogs, however playful they may be that day.
And to climb means making sure you do not
tumble to the bottom by stepping on a flimsy plank . . .
That is, if you are completely sober . . .
Octavia's flat
has no rooms:
a train car is Octavia's flat,
a gallery of paintings
and statues
and piles of wondrous art . . .
But Octavia has a barrel-like table with two tumblers
and two chairs,
and tidbits of white cheese on black bread.
But the two dogs are circling
and they may snatch the white cheese on black bread . . .
I say: Octavia!
Please
send the dogs away from here . . .
Octavia smiles:
Saadi, in Paris you were so unhappy with having just one dog and
    now two dogs surround you!
*

Wait, wait.
I'll bring you the whisky right away!

London, 07.05.2012

These two poems above are from the collection *Qasa'id Harefield*
(*Poems of Harefield on the Hill*). More poems translated from this
collection can be read on pages 66 and page 111.

KHALED MATTAWA

Skyping with Saadi, Channeling Li Po

E very now and then I have the chance to chat with the great Iraqi poet Saadi Youssef. We exchange news, talk poetry and more often than not commiserate on the bad shape of our homelands. Also, while Saadi is speaking I often find myself listening to an unwritten chapter of modern Arabic poetry, as if a time portal has opened up to a wondrous and intriguing past I knew nothing of. This time I skyped with Saadi to query him about lines in poems of his that I was translating. When we were finished I asked him what he was working on.

To be sure, Saadi is always writing poems, sometimes several poems a day. But he's also always working on something else, perhaps assembling a new diwan from among his most recent poems. This time, he told me he's translating the great Chinese poet Li Po (702-762 AD), also known as Li Bai.

I was very fascinated. I teach Li Po in a comparative poetics class at Michigan. In fact, it was Li Po who led me to discover earlier Chinese texts such as the *Book of Songs* (Shi Jing) and the *Songs of the South* (Chu Si), both are works of astounding beauty.

Saadi asked me if I was familiar with "The River Merchant's Wife", Ezra Pound's translation of a poem by Li Po. I said I knew the poem and the story of how Pound stumbled upon Japanese versions of Chinese poetic masterpieces among the notebooks of the Japan scholar Ernest Fenollosa (1853-1908). From these translations Pound published the collection *Cathay* in 1915. The volume includes "River Merchant's Wife", but is attributed to Rihaku not to Li Po – Rihaku being Li Po's Japanese name.

Khaled Mattawa visiting Saadi Youssef in Harefield, photo Samuel Shimon

As we talked, I looked for *Cathay*. Pound, as turned out, titled the book *Cathay, Translations by Ezra Pound: For the Most Part from the Chinese of Rihaku, from the notes of the late Ernest Fenollosa, and the Decipherings of the Professors Mori and Ariga*. Nonetheless, the poems were attributed to Pound as their author, and remain so today. "River Merchant's Wife" is one of the most anthologized poems in the English language and is always included among Pound's compositions. In college I encountered the poem as belonging to Ezra Pound, no questions asked.

Saadi then told me that was the impression the great Iraqi poet Badr Shakir Al-Sayyab (1926–1964) had when he translated "The River Merchant's Wife". Al-Sayyab included it in *Qasa'id mukhtara min al-shi'r al-'alami al-hadith* (A Selection of International Modern Poems), an anthology he published in 1955. According to Saadi, Al-Sayyab's translation of the poem, which I have not been able to locate, was in metrical Arabic verse, or taf'ila, the new poetic form that he and the other great Iraqi poet of the period, Nazik Al-Malaika, had pioneered.

Li Po's "A River Merchant's Wife" in Sayyab's resonant Arabic based on Pound's English verse is doubtlessly a remarkable poem emblematic of modern poetry in the twentieth century, where translation played an essential role in freeing languages all over the world and the poets working in them from inherited conventions that seemed to stifle creativity. Pound felt this need to bust loose from the prosody and diction of English poetry written in the late 19th century that was choking his voice, as did other writers at the time. Modernist critic Hugh Kenner reports that in 1912 Pound visited Ford Maddox Ford, a writer Pound greatly admired, and showed him his poems. Ford reacted by rolling on the floor in mock agony in response to Pound's overwrought poetic language. It is no secret that Pound's discovery of Asian poetry, and his translations of Chinese, freed him tremendously and gave him a sense of lyricism he would not have discovered otherwise. Plenty of evidence also shows that T S Eliot also benefited from translation. Translating French Symbolist poets helped him adhere to Pound's advice to seek poetic beauty by composing "in the sequence of the musical phrase, not in sequence of a metronome".

As such, Li Po's "A River Merchant's Wife" as it reached young Saadi Youssef in 1955 (via Sayyab via Pound) was a powerful poetic cocktail that mixed Chinese classicism with Anglophone and Arabic modernist poetics. And complicated as the poem's genealogy may have been it was doubtlessly a seamless lyric due to its clear images and its understated expressions of emotion. Saadi went on to say that "*Risalah min zawjat tajer al-nahr*" (A Letter from the River Merchant's Wife), attributed to Ezra Pound, inspired him in 1956 to write a poem of his own, titled "Ilhah" (Insistence).

I knew "Insistence" quite well as I myself translated it some time in the late 1990s. In "Insistence" Saadi offers the persona of a young river merchant who is filled with longing for his wife, matching that of Li Po's female speaker. Saadi's poet speaker implores the captain, Salim Marzouq, to take him on his ship:

Salim Marzouq, take me   on a ship
on a ship. Take my eyes for ransom . . . I'll do what you wish
except what women are supposed to.
Salim Marzouq   my sad wife
is a prisoner in her father's house
in a village near Sihan, arid without palms.

Saadi takes the modernist appropriation of Li Po to its logical con-
clusion. He localizes the tender feelings of Li Po's female speaker
and responds to them with a local male voice rising from the marsh-
lands of Basra.

Decades after writing "Insistence" Saadi discovered that the poem
that inspired him to write "Insistence" and other poems of the period actually belonged to Li Po, not Ezra Pound. And now six
decades after "Insistence", Saadi is hard at work on a translation of
poems by the great master Li Po, based on English translation. "Li
Po's poetry is rooted in modern poetry, even in Arabic poetry," he
explained. Indeed! And when I said earlier that Saadi is always working on something, this time it delights me no end to see one of the
masters of modern Arabic poetry renewing his voice by rediscov-
ering his complicated poetic roots.

Saadi's new poems echo this intricately braided inheritance, intersecting his subtle voice with Li Po's acute sensitivity to nature.
We also have the solace of drink, the pangs of solitude and the self-
deprecating tone that made Li Po's poetry so endearing and moving,
and so modern. But unlike Li Po, who tends to ease us off his painful
moments at the end of his poems, Saadi sometimes works his imag-
istic impressions into intense dramatic conclusions as in the poems
"Woodpecker" and "Morning Scene".

Imaging Saadi as the Li Po of our modern times, I see his poems
as combinations of brush strokes that dip inward into emotion and
outward into nature, and from this intense exchange of image and
disclosure emerge poignant renderings of an extraordinary inner
life, rich in empathy and resonant with transcendence.

Find us on Facebook
https://www.facebook.com/BanipalMagazine

HUSSEIN BIN HAMZA

Young Poet
Turns Eighty

Saadi Youssef's project began, developed, ripened, and reached fruition without his ever attempting to describe himself as a "great poet". Saadi Youssef is of course a great poet, but this description is consistent with the vibrant experimentation that has accompanied his long trajectory in writing. This experimentation has afforded the Iraqi poet a type of perennial youth and has guaranteed for him continual high standing in both the poetry of his pioneering contemporaries and that of successive generations. In this sense he is a "great friend" of what Arab poets have written in the past decades and the founder owner of a poetic project who deserves to garner true, subdued, and tangible beatification reminiscent of his true, subdued, and tangible style of poem. The author of *Qasa'id Aqall Samtan* (Quieter Poems, 1979) prefers a poem he refers to as a "material poem" – one written in a tangible and molecular language that avoids rhetorical drowsiness and emotional anguish. It is true that this type of poem does not lack lyricism, but its narrative flow dissolves the lyrical (originally softly rendered) and buries it within the lexicon of realism and its ordinary diction. From the outset Saadi Youssef moved toward a kind of *taf'ila* poem that was restless, wistful and with an irregular metre that helped liberate quickly him from the "terror" of traditional metre and made it easier for him subsequently to attain a rhythmic stress pattern virtually devoid of metre. More importantly, it moved him away from the overblown descriptions that characterized the pioneers' version of modernity, a substantial part of which were the view of the poet as a prophet, depicting mythological worlds and providing universal visions and insights.

Saadi was a contemporary of al-Sayyab, and both men belonged to the Iraqi Communist Party. *Shi'r* magazine published a poem by Saadi in its first issue in 1957. His early poems flourished in the classical metres of Arabic (or *'Umudi*) poetry and in the nascent free verse *taf'ila* poem that was coming into vogue then among its Iraqi pioneers. He seemed, however, someone who placed one foot in the lexicon of the new modernism and the other foot in the dictionary that the prose poem would subsequently propose. This was an early blend of a rhythm that did not slight the meanings that formed it and of a desire to narrate, expatiate, portray, and ponder. It was a blend in which the rhythmic element was reduced in favour of narration and prose. The poet seemed to play with the plentiful gaps in his metre until this tendency became a personal style and his artistic signature. It was a blend of subdued rhetoric that is written in the very language and sensibility of "the little man", as was aptly described by the Syrian critic Mohammad Jamal Barout. It was a blend that made the poet a poetic citizen rather than a prophet or a leader. It was a blend in which the rhythm was minimized to the point that we began to read Saadi's poetry without noticing how indebted its composition was to the *taf'ila* poem. It was a blend that the late Mahmoud Darwish subsequently praised:

"Since I began reading the poetry of Saadi Youssef, that poetry has been the poetry closest to my poetic sensibility. His diaphanous poem has the clarity of a water colour painting, and its subdued voice contains the rhythm of daily life. I might dare to suppose that he – without writing the prose poem that is prevalent today – has become one of its great inspirations, because it navigates an expressive climate that Saadi's poetry infused into the aesthetic sensibility after perfecting the art of blending lyricism with narration."

The poet began with a little debut offering entitled *al-Qursan* (The Pirate, 1952), which included verses with multiple rhyme words. Then he mixed couplets with free verse (*taf'ilat*) in his second collection *Ughniyat Laysat lil-Akharin* (Songs Not For Others, 1955). Metre did not deter him from finding his way to a lexicon that collected vocabulary with an amount of contemplation and deliberation that made the poetic line less boisterous, more detailed, more intensely concerned with with what is seen in all its overlooked detail. This lexicon was completely present in the title of his fifth collection, *Qasa'id Mari'ya* (Visible Poems, 1965), where "visible" meant that the poem would be more palpable and composed of an idea that could be recounted without drowsy lethargy or gratuitous talk and with the poem being the product of a clear personal experience and without being indebted to the drone of an insipid rhythm and an overflow of meaningless piffle.

That effort was also present at the offset of his collection *Nihayat Al-Shamal Al-Ifriqi* (The Ends of North Africa, 1972) in the form of a passage by the Greek poet [Giorgos] Seferis that seems more like a concentrated condensation of Saadi's poetic aspirations: "I want nothing more than to speak simply, to be granted that grace. / Because we've loaded even our song with so much music that it's slowly sinking / and we've decorated our art so much that its features have been eaten away by gold / and it's time to say our few words because tomorrow our soul sets sail." Saadi's poem developed more and more from one collection to the next. It rid itself of that excessive "ornamentation" that spoils a poem, it rid itself of the loud music that spoils the serenity of the poem and the deep machinations of its meaning. Saadi's poem has been able to find itself, its scenarios, as well as its future contexts.

His poem "The Last Communist," as he refers to himself, was a forward-looking poem, and perhaps the early absence in it of metaphysical excess, existential sloppiness, and visionary philosophizing presaged the future to the degree that it was a testimony to a present that the poet was attempting to write in a way that was different back then.

Saadi Youssef – just like Nizar Qabbani, Salah Abdul Sabour and Mohammad Al-Maghout – has worked to create straightforward lexicon, metaphors, images, and worlds fashioned from this directness, which applies also to the use of language, the imagination, the lived event, and the political stance, too. For this reason, it is certainly not odd that poets of subsequent generations have found in Saadi's poetry a sounding board for their experiments. Returning to the Arabic poetry that has been written from the end of the 1970s to the present, we find many experiments that are directly or indirectly indebted to his style of poem. We may possibly not be exaggerating much if we attribute a large portion of the production of Mahmoud Darwish during his last twenty years to intensely clever and original uses of Saadi Youssef's experiment. We also find similar, diverse traces in the output of a number of the most important Arab poets of the 1970s. It is easy to trace Saadi's influences in the poetry of Amjad Nasser, Zakaria Mohammed, Ghassan Zaqtan, Riad Al-Saleh Al-Hussein, in addition to tens of Iraqi poets. It is true that those poets have been able to turn Saadi's influences into personal and individual accomplishments, but the fingerprint of the poet of *Janat Al-Mansiyyat* (Paradise of the Forgotten Things, 1993) are visible in their poetry. In addition to that, most of what has been written and that is being written in the genre called *al-shi'r al-yawmi* (everyday poetry) or *qasidat al-tafasil* (the poem of details) has its roots, tastes, and fragrances in Saadi's language, which favours precision, realistic documentation, visual cues, contemplation of places, inanimate objects, and the motion of life and its transient details. This is an opportunity to say that Saadi Youssef's poem, which is almost oral and spoken, is also an eloquent poem. It is the descendant of deep-rooted poetic classics. For this reason, he discovers for his tangible, material, quotidian language a strong connection that links it to the language of Imru' al-Qais, who is present, along with other Jahili and Abbasid era poets, for example, in more than one of his poems and has even appeared in the title of an entire poetry collection by Saadi, *Hafid Imri' al-Qais* (Imru' al-Qais's Grandson, 2006).

However, the poet with "the subdued rhetoric in modern Arabic poetry", as the title of a book on his poetry by Iraqi critic Fatima Al-Muhsin described him, is not always subdued.

He has stirred many a controversy with things that he said in his poetry, his articles and in statements that he made and especially after the American invasion of Iraq in 2003, and more recently in his scathing criticism of the so-called Arab Spring. In one his more recent interviews Saadi said: "At a time of great change, or what seems like great change, a poet is not to abandon public responsibility and should enter the field of turmoil with a loud voice and with varied aesthetic." He is "the last communist", as he referred to himself in a complete book of poems with that same title. A communist in his own way, and an Iraqi in his own way as well, for he never saw a divide between his practice of poetry and his political stands.

A large portion of Saadi's poetry can be read as autobiographical or as fragments of his life that have transitioned to his poem, because it is prepared to welcome elements of personal life that occur in prose passages of daily life. The poet himself has transformed his stays in numerous Arab and foreign places of exile into material for poetry. He has brilliantly teased details and novel scenes into the space of his poem, which during the last two decades has become short and compressed. It generally ends with a clausula or punch line that illuminates the lines composing the poem. The poem itself conveys the poet's experience, astonishment, isolation, premonitions, desires, and ideological positions even as the names of cities like Damascus, Beirut, Amman, Tangier, Aden, Tunis, Batina, Sidi Bel Abbès, London, New York, Paris, Nicosia, and Moscow follow each other in succession. But all this has been regulated by impressions and political political impressions and views, and those cities and places have provided a space for a blend of scenes, ideas, and current topics with memories and former lives from his his birthplace, the village of Hamdan in southern Iraq, or from Basra, where he studied before he moved to Baghdad, as well as from his long period of living abroad in places of exile. Thus numerous cities, moods, and sceneries merge in a single poem occasionally, so much so that an entire poetry collection is dedicated to Tangier in Morocco, for example.

In this context, let us not forget his poetry translations, most of which seem to have been experiments that he admired or that he would have liked to have written himself. This can be seen in the strong influences on his poetry by Ritsos, Lorca, and Cafavy, for example. Perhaps the practice of translation itself revealed to him how texts that contain superfluous eloquence, pleasantries, and pronounced rhythms lose a lot when they are translated to other languages. His poetry in general and his most recent collections have especially benefited from his translating. They were written in in a concrete and pointed language "that does not lose its intrinsic value in other languages," as he himself noted.

Saadi Youssef has turned eighty, and his complete works of poetry are appearing in seven volumes, while his poem itself continues to preserve its vitality, on the one hand, and its influence on poetry being written today, on the other. The poet has just turned eighty, but he is still a "young poet".

TRANSLATED BY WILLIAM M HUTCHINS

MONA ANIS

One of the most valuable friendships

Mona Anis and Saadi Youssef in Cairo, January 1990

As we celebrate Saadi Youssef's 80th birthday anniversary, I think of the first time I saw him in person. That was in Cairo 25 years ago, before the Iraqi invasion of Kuwait, the two Gulf Wars (1991 and 2003) and before being an Iraqi was construed as tragic. The quintessential tragic hero in the Arab world until then was the Palestinian and at that time Saadi doubled as a Palestinian.

Thus, when the PLO held a large celebration in Cairo in 1990, presided over by Yasser Arafat, to commemorate 25 years since the beginning of the Palestinian Revolution, and to decorate Palestinian writers and intellectuals who served the cause, the one non-Palestinian honoured along with Palestinian luminaries such as Emile Habibi, Mahmoud Darwish and Samih al-Qassim was Saadi Youssef, or l'Akhdar Ben Youssef, the name Saadi coined for his alter ego since the publication of his famous poem "L'Akhdar Ben Youssef and His Concerns" in 1972.

Al-Akhdar, meaning "the green" in Arabic, has become Saadi Youssef's "other", an "other" facing oppression and tyranny in different places of the Arab world. Once a North African (often Algerian or Moroccan), al-Akhdar had assumed his Palestinian identity in 1976 during the siege and massacres at Tel el-Zaatar refugee camp in Lebanon.

I have been a great admirer of Saadi's poetry for as long as I remember, but it was during the winter of 1990 that we first met and started a friendship that developed over the years to become one of the most valuable friendships in my life. Through this friendship, I became more aware of another Saadi, the Iraqi Saadi hiding behind the many masks of al-Akhdar, and it was this friendship that brought me closer to Saadi's native Iraq.

When Saadi Youssef was in Cairo in 1993, I interviewed him with my senior colleague the late Egyptian critic Farouq Abdel-Qadir. It was published in *Rose al-Yusuf* magazine and a shortened English version, which I translated, appeared in *Al-Ahram Weekly*.

I am very pleased to contribute the following translations of four of Saadi's poems for this celebration in Banipal.

SAADI YOUSSEF

Four poems

TRANSLATED BY MONA ANIS

PLANTING

Do not waste your time
It's more difficult than you think:
True, there is a clay pot, precisely in the corner where it's sunny
True, the mud is red
and you know how to control drops of water
Yet the palm seedling will never grow in your room
The palm will never breath like you,
even if your breath grows quieter
even if your breath is silenced.

***

But when night comes
and you close your eyelids
and water flows to where water is transparent
the palm tree will come to you
tall
supple
blue . . .

LOYALTY

From one country to another you shall wander
From one woman to another you shall escape
From one desert to another
But the thread flying the kite

will always remain the taut thread
tied to the palm tree
from where your first kite flew.

WHAT?

What made singing
bitter
until we held silent

***

What made wine glasses
cut our hands
until we bled?

***

In the dream
even the young tree enters
heavy with knives?

***

Did I say: we are finished?

BAGHDAD

My friend said to me: How does Baghdad appear before your
   eyes?
I said: The city is one with its people.
He said: But you are them . . .
I said: Then, I shall seek kin other than them
and head to another Baghdad.

These four poems were written in Summer 1993 in Amman, and are
   included in the collection *The Lonely Man Wakes up*, collected in
   Four Movements, an anthology published in Cairo in 1997.

PETER MONEY

From Where I Sit

From where I sit, I can think about the Middle East (as we consider it) in a second. (Maybe we all should take a second and think about a place far from us?) In a glance I ponder the people and the geography, the history and artifacts, struggles, loves and contributions – music, architecture, literature. This is not from a glance at the newspaper headlines or a Tweet (although those things bring perspectives of the Middle East also – as well as news from my own home – to a certain form of the public eye). The glance I mean to convey to you is of my mountain. I live facing a mountain, and this mountain has "figured" in my rapport with Saadi Youssef. I moved here in August of 2001.

James Baldwin and Martin Luther King famously wrote and spoke using a mountain as a symbol. Baldwin's novel *Go Tell It On The Mountain* begins with a simple short lyric that anticipates backward and forward thinking: "I look down the line, / And I wondered." MLK's "Mountaintop" speech was, as we accept through history, his last but its vision continues to serve as an abiding projection. For me, the mountain of my present location is part of the reason I have come to know Saadi Youssef. What's the relationship between Saadi Youssef and my hometown mountain, you ask?

Every day I look out and I see a pyramid. In this glance I am transported, albeit through my imagination, to the subject of my childhood dreams. As a seven-year-old boy, I wanted to visit the pyramids in Egypt. Nearly twenty years later I did so, traveling on my own. I was a recent college graduate (from the American "Mid-West" we call it here) and I knew I should see life beyond my "white picket fence". I had, based on a semester in Ireland, wanted to become a writer – although I had been storing poems in a toy safe since I was seven. In traveling I would come in contact with more stories; I would find my poems. My Huckleberry Finn expedition was a trip

Saadi Youssef, with Sinan Antoon (l) and Peter Money (r) in New York

around the world and, like Huck, I noticed that all people are not free and easy all of the time – anywhere. I paid for my journey by working as a labourer, setting tables, serving, washing dishes, painting houses (once with a racially abusive crew) – and by cashing a meagre amount of the life insurance my parents had dropped in my hands after I turned eighteen. I suppose I had already realized there was no need for insurance. There was no "assurance", only the best moments of every day. To most Americans it's probably true that other regions are a blur – complicated by reason of distances and parochial attitudes. To me, the Egypt of my imagination was a representation of a vast and complex region I would only begin to come to know.

Understand, I wanted to know about the lives of others beyond my own region. When one of our more infamous presidents started talking in ignorantly combative terms about Iraq, I wondered instead if I could focus on a distant human face – through poetry. This was 2002. Somewhat randomly I searched the internet for articles about poets from Iraq and I was naturally drawn to Saadi Youssef. A fellow "modernist"! Translator of Walt Whitman! And then I read his poetry and there I found Abe Lincoln, New Orleans (a personal favourite), birds bending a stalk. Saadi Youssef was my poet. His poems even reminded me of my own mentor's work (Allen Ginsberg, of the notoriously banned "Howl"), by way of verve, and of my favourite William Carlos Williams, by way of the shorter poems (and Williams was Ginsberg's mentor). Needless to say, I reached out to Saadi. To my astonishment, he was there and responded.

I had, to use James Baldwin's beginning, "looked down the line, / And . . . wondered." What is it to be another's shoes? What a joy to find affinity in someone far away! The "Middle" East became Near East through Saadi's correspondence with me. Together, it's safe to say, we lamented about the state of his country – and sometimes about the state of mine. And because I was attuned, I heard Shakir Mustafa (translator and editor of the important *Contemporary Iraqi Fiction* anthology, published by Syracuse) on the radio while I was driving, and he put me in touch with Sinan Antoon. Sinan, to my surprise, was teaching "just up the road" – and, although at a greater distance, we had the same mountain in our view. A few years later with Sinan, at a PEN event, I was introduced to Saadi in person. His infectious beaming smile and hardy enthusiasm was an immediate welcome. Simply, to an extent, we were related.

MORNING SCENE

In dawn's twilight
the forest mist is a white blue.
The birds are voiceless
and on the Grand Union Canal
  ghost boats loom.
A string from a chimney snakes
  up the sky.
No soft rustle from the trees,
not even one flutter of wings,
  or eye lashes
as if the moment is frozen,
as if the world has yet to be.

London, 30.05.2012

Translated by Khaled Mattawa
from the collection
Poems of Harefield on the Hill

When one of our more infamous presidents started talking in ignorantly combative terms about Iraq, I wondered instead if I could focus on a distant human face – through poetry."

By this point in time I had published *To day – Minutes only*, a title inspired by my reading of Saadi's poetry. This was a small letterpress limited edition and copies disappeared without fanfare. Nevertheless, I had hoped it would help to initiate a discussion. Sometimes films and books can do these things! *To day – Minutes only* is what I consider to be a "dialogue" with Saadi (much of it referencing his poem "That Rainy Day"). Later, in different forms, a CD (Blue Square) and an anthology published by City Lights featured the poem. At this time I also published Saadi's poems "A Woman", "Still Life", "The Tormented (or The Colony)" in the literary journal I founded and edited at a small college where I was teaching. The journal was adamantly called *Across Borders*. (Few people outside select locations in the United States were aware that border check points had been set up within the US, such as there was within sight of my mountain.)

It had been my ambition (unfulfilled as of this date) to write a children's picture story about Saadi Youssef's life and poetry. I thought this could be a way to ease tensions and pain: allowing children to experience poetry across borders, so to speak. I had, gratefully, Ferial Ghazoul's biography to study and Khaled Mattawa's introduction to the first Graywolf Press publication of Saadi Youssef poems. It's worth noting that I quote Khaled Mattawa at the beginning of *To day – Minutes only*: "concerted efforts in patient silence" – which is a little like Baldwin's looking down the line and wondering.

It is in the wondering that our relationships initiate belief in the humanity of our kindred efforts. I have Margaret Obank to thank, as well as Shakir Mustafa, Sinan Antoon, Khaled Mattawa, PEN, Banipal, and our editors at Graywolf Press. Several years later, *To day – Minutes only* resides as the Middle section (remember? "Middle East". . .) of a three-part shout across the universe I call a poetry drone. I still believe that if there is to be shouting, and blurring of lines, and confusion in chaos . . . then there is also to be a time for dialogue and meditation (my *American Drone* would correct the wrongs and provide breath, and song). In 2012 I'd had the pleasure, with Sinan, of seeing *Nostalgia, My Enemy* published (Graywolf) and distributed through Farrar Strauss & Giroux.

At the moment, during the precise timing of my typing (an act of being alive), a plane flies over this mountain. Both plane and mountain become symbols. They can't help it now. At one glance this mountain is bold with the early morning sunshine (from "the East") casting shadows: gold and black in the tufts of green. Minutes later fog from the large river a few miles away, not unlike the Mississippi, wraps a scarf around my mountain. As I wait, this becomes a veil, or a shroud, or a blank piece of paper. A blank screen. What will be revealed here?

I am pleased to say the mountains that matter in our imagination are here to stay. This is an observation Saadi makes in his poem "The Glance": "Our loss is not the earth / for the earth will stay, / it stayed before us, / it will stay after us, / earth of the singers . . ."

One more thing. One last word, for now: during our time at PEN Sinan and Saadi and I hung out, several stories above the street below, in an empty old ballroom. There happened to be a piano there. Because Saadi had written "AMERICA, AMERICA" – in which he writes: "How long will I walk to reach my home" and then: "A stranger becomes afraid. / Have no fear, dear horse. / No fear of the wolves of the wild, / No fear, for the land is my land" . . .

I sat and played the blues (not great blues, mind you, but blues only the three of us – and the PEN interns in the kitchen – would hear; blues my teacher and "howler" taught me to sing). But I did it for Saadi, and for Sinan, and for me, and for anyone who was trying to find reasons to celebrate, through the awkward and sorrowful wails, our – and others' – potentially joyful existence. May it be through this sort of song.

New England, September 2014

JACK HIRSCHMAN

A POEM FOR SAADI

THE WAY TO END WAR

When the planet's as it is today
chockablock with wars
at every click of the computer,
turn of the dial,
button on the teevee remote,

and greed and religions' hatreds
hatch eggs of grief everywhere
like deathballs, and old ladies
are stamping on throwaway
soda cans worth pennies in the street

and fascist capitalism gives us
a digitalized semi-robotic
comic strip life with a laugh a minute
when that big busty bimbo
takes it all off,

how cam anyone say that communism
isn't necessary? It's failed, of course,
                              NOT!

It's the way to end war! The only
hope left. The rest is waiting
for atomicide.

photo: Samuel Shimon

Saadi Youssef:

Now we are a shattered country, there is no more Iraq for the time being.

STEPHEN WATTS, with Cristina Viti, interviews SAADI YOUSSEF at his home on the outskirts of London.

For me, Saadi Youssef is quite simply a great poet, a universal poet. He has reached this by means of rare lyric calm and integrity of complex truths in the face of the world and his is a superbly achieved poetry. It may well have been beyond his imagining as a child of ten in a village beside a river full of history south of Basra (the age he began to think of writing poetry) that as a man of eighty he would find himself living in exile, if in some composure and calm, in a village outside London. That is his story of migration, exemplary of the experience of so many people in the late 20th and 21st centuries, a story that weaves through the language of his poetry.

I therefore wanted to interview him in his home and I hoped also to reflect his experience in his own words, in his own English and against a politicised English that has often resulted in arbitrary boundaries throughout the Middle East. For Saadi's poetry is the opposite of drawing arbitrary boundaries and is very much to do with the deep expression of freedom. The work of his poetry is not an easy achievement, and perhaps I have failed to bring over his words well enough in these edited transcripts: much truth slips through our fingers and tongues during the recording of a voice. It is his poetry in the end that manages to reach the deeper truths and to give expression to them with beautiful lyric calm and rare intensity and I would urge the reader to go to this poetry and to keep returning to it.

STEPHEN WATTS

Stephen Watts and Saadi Youssef during the interview, photo Samuel Shimon

Stephen Watts: I am going to start by asking you about your childhood years because you've written such beautiful poems about those times and places.

Saadi Youssef: Yes. Well, I was born in Basra, or just south of Basra, and it was a great oasis of date palms, rivulets and rivers, so in my childhood the trees, the palm trees and the rivers were very important for me and, later, I did indeed depict these things in my poems. Back then, we were a poor family and we fought hard for our bread. I finished university and so on, but it wasn't an easy life at that time. However, childhood is always a gold mine, you can draw on it as

> ## The principle of lyric is very sensual in poetry, which has always had to be sung and performed

you like with very nice colours and memories. And, later, at a certain age you need it, this childhood, because it sustains you through harshness and lies, because it's more attached to the beautiful side of life . . . and perhaps, well I hope, this shows in some of the poems that I wrote later on.

SW: You have a poem, I think it's from an early collection, maybe from when you were living in Algeria in the 1960s; it's called "Shatt al-Arab" and consists of three dreams. It's a very beautiful poem (translated into English by Khaled Mattawa). I imagine that you are recalling episodes from your childhood:

"Dream 1. On nights of torment and sorrow / its waters saturate my pillow / and it comes like the smell of moss / with green steps / to touch my right palm / with a jasmine sprig: / Wake up . . . / I am the river . . ."[1]

Your poetry, early and late, is full of references to rivers, to the flowing of water. The places where you grew up show in so much of your work, in later poems too, always . . .

SY: There is also something else about my childhood. Our place was on the Shatt al-Arab river that flows between Iraq and Iran and eventually into the sea. When we were kids we used to cross over to the other side and back; there are reeds on the Iranian side and we'd go across in very, very small boats to the other side, into and through the reeds; and we'd go walking to Abadan and other places. I had relatives there and I would visit them and then go back. It was wonderful. Sometimes it would be for one day, sometimes I'd stay there for two days or more, with a tiny boat like this (Saadi extends his arms and we all laugh). A brother of my grandfather lived on

> When I was about 11 . . . I started by
> learning the rules of classical Arabic
> poetry, which is very hard . . .

the other side, and two of the brothers came to settle in Iraq, back then at a time when there was another Arab princedom on the other side. My grandfather bought land on the Iraqi side, with borders and guards and everything. Back then it wasn't like now; it was a river for all, with Arabs on both sides.

SW: Did you know your grandfather well?

SY: Yes, I knew him well. I knew him very well. I used to visit him regularly, every week or more than that. He always used to talk to me about his adventures: for example, he spent six years in India – because he had killed someone – six years living in Bombay (as it was called then) or thereabouts until there was some change from the court and he was able to return. He was always dreaming about India, about its magic. He had green eyes, I remember, and he and I used to go fishing together in the early morning and he'd put a kind of a cage down in the water for catching fish . . .

SW: It's a lovely image for a poem, for poetry, that, of letting a cage down into deeper waters and going back later to pull it up . . .

SY: Yes (laughs) . . . And you know that before all the pollution there used to be a particular kind of fish in the Shatt al-Arab ; I think it's called a pomfret, living there between fresh water and sea water.

Cristina Viti: That's also a lovely description of poetry, between fresh and sea water . . .

SW: Saadi, when do you remember writing your first poem, or first wanting to write a poem?

SY: It was about 1944 or '45 . . . when I was about 11 . . .

SW: *You were very young . . .*

SY: I started by learning the rules of classical Arabic poetry, which is very hard. It's a very rich metrical system; there are 16 rules of metre in our poetry in Arabic, far fewer in Latin languages. So first I had to train my ear to these 16 metres of poetry and then I started imitating. The first Arab poet I started to imitate was Imru al-Qais from the 6th century, using his rhyme and metre, and then others. It was very useful for me. Until now people are always surprised at my mastery of those metrical rules; and sometimes I still do my version of them. One of my poems was called "Imru al-Qais's Grandson"[2]. Actually, my first collection was quite traditional in form, but I changed the rhyme every six verses. It was a sea adventure, this work, and I think it was influenced by my grandfather. It was called *The Pirate*.

SW: *I wrote a review of your book* Without An Alphabet, Without A Face *– translated and introduced by Khaled Mattawa – and in it I said you were a poet of sea journeys, even though in a way it's not true, but I wasn't aware then of what you've just talked about now . . .*

SY: I have always been very interested in sea travels, I have books of and about Sir Francis Drake, the pirate privateer, then I have works by Conrad and Melville, and I read sea adventures. Sometimes I have made sea voyages too, for example, from Barcelona to Beirut or from Alexandria, or I sailed from Latakia to Odessa, so sea life was always giving me something of a clear breath, elements of nature. Cristina is even pointing to my wall here and there's a poem on the wall, a poem about an old pirate, so all this matters to me! Well, I think it's called "The Moment". Other writers also meant a lot to me – Robert Louis Stevenson for instance. And then some of the places I've lived in were on the Mediterranean, and some of the poets I've translated are from the Mediterranean, such as Ungaretti from Alexandria, and Cavafy, and so on. Once, when I went to Elsinore [Helsingør], to "Hamlet's Castle", seeing the staircase and the hall . . . and then I went down to the sea, where Hamlet would have boarded the ship . . . ah . . . the sea! I was more

Hamlet is always with me

influenced by the sea, the waves and the way the sea flowed onto the rocks. I wrote three poems about Hamlet's balcony in Elsinore's castle [Ed: two of which, "Elsinore, Hamlet's castle" and "Hamlet's Balcony", were published in *Banipal 15/16*, translated by Sargon Boulus]. Perhaps I should research Shakespeare, but really I'm more attached just to *Hamlet* because it has so many questions that still matter. More for me than *The Tempest*. No, *Hamlet* is always with me. I buy new copies of *Hamlet*, in new editions and with notes. I think there are three here in my home now. But none of this is a forced march, there's nothing of Genghis Khan's forced march for days and days on end!

SW: I'm trying to remember a wonderful but sad poem looking back on the Communist Party in Iraq . . . the one that starts in the wide air and ends shadowed in the corners of a room.

SY: That's "Genesis '34", about the founding of the Iraqi Communist Party in 1934. I think Sinan Antoon translated it, or perhaps it's in the book *Troubled Waters* . . .

We look for this first little book of Saadi's in English and finding it, open it and turn to the poem "Departure of 82" and then to "Exhaustion". Then we open Nostalgia, My Enemy *and the first poem we see there is "Hamlet's Balcony". While we don't in fact find the poem we're looking for, Saadi recalls Pasolini when we chance upon the poem "Tonight I imitate Pasolini".*

SY: Once I went to a café in Rome where Pasolini used to go . . . they showed me his football team T-shirt (*CV: He was captain of the Actors and Singers football team*). Ah yes ! Pasolini . . . I do have a real regard for Italian poetry. That other poem, "Genesis '34" . . . on slow trains . . . I remember – Sinan published it on a website[3]. . . It says more than just about the Iraqi Communist Party, it goes further into our history.

SW: In the book Troubled Waters *there is a long poem that you wrote – was it in Beirut? – "Post Cards From Hajj Omrane", marking the start of the Iran–Iraq war and plunging further back into history, and this is coming back to us now . . .*

SY: Yes, that's right. And even now people think it's my masterpiece. It's a very important poem, I wrote it in Addis Ababa in maybe 1984 or '85; it goes back in our histories over thousands of years, but also it talks about the Iran–Iraq War, which was ignited when Iranians occupied Iraqi positions. It was a very, very painful time and much of our dark destiny started there in that war. And now we are a shattered country, there is no more Iraq for the time being. What the Americans have done imitating Garcia Marquez's *One Hundred Years Of Solitude*, is to set up One Hundred Years Of Occupation. Ten now, and perhaps another ninety to go, until the last drop of oil has gone.

SW: The Iran–Iraq war is one that's very little considered in the west, in UK or America . . . And then, later, you wrote that wonderful poem "America, America" . . .

SY: Yes, yes. That poem is one of my best works[4]. It was heavily influenced by both American culture and people. I'm full of respect for the American people and for popular heritage, for Whitman and the others. Now, sometimes, when I go to Greenwich Village for a month or so, I like to stay among the new jazz musicians and singers. There was a bar where Dylan Thomas drank on his last visit, the White Horse I think it's called. There's a photo of him there, taken just before he died, and he died young, only thirty-nine.

SW: In all your poetry there is a sense of freedom and lyric action. It's there in your poetry, so deeply achieved or embedded . . .

SY: That's one point, but I think another is that poetry has embedded in itself the responsibility of refreshing and even entertaining. That is very essential in poetry, and to art in general. We write to make people happy . . . to help them see nature . . . to let people see wonderful colours . . . So I keep trying for this freshness in poetry . . . Even if our lives are really too difficult, in art I respect this fundamental message of survival, of art for fresh air, of poetry as

> When I read Cavafy, what made me even more attached to him was the strict system of language he strived to achieve; the poetic sentence of Cavafy was constructed in a very difficult and strict way. My respect is for that precision

an antidote to the gloom, the difficult times in our lives. When we carry a poem or a book of poems close to our flesh, as a talisman or as a shield – Cristina's right when she said that just now – we can go beyond the pain. That is how we make our lives richer.

SW: One of the other beautiful things about your poetry is that you write both short poems and long poems and you've done this throughout your life. I'm thinking of the some of the titles of your longer poems: "The Ends of the African North", "The Itinerary Through Three Cafés", "The Trees of Ithaca", "Post Cards From Hajj Omrane"⁵, "Thank You Imru ul-Qais"⁶, "How L'Akhdar Ben Youssef Wrote His Last Poem" . . .

SY: In shorter poems I respect what Paul Valéry said that "The first verse is from God", but longer poems need to be planned, at least have a very rough plan. I have to go through a sort of structure, to make a rough plan for a longer poem, in order to have control. An artist acquires a certain power to organise certain things, even to control how things cohere, but loosely, not in a strict way. So, I have one, two, three, four parts. At least in the beginning I have some vague idea of a plan, a sort of a sea chart, before I can let loose the words or allow them come out.

SW: I want to listen more to you, to let you talk . . . but I also want to ask you about your translations of certain poets. You have translated a wide range of poets, very different to each other in some ways, but in other ways close too. Ungaretti and Cavafy, Lorca, Ritsos, Popa, and there are more . . . There's something of you in each of them . . .

SY: Yes. For me the principle of lyric is very sensual in poetry. Poetry has always had to be sung and performed. It still is sometimes; well, just think of the French singers. For that reason I think you are right, there's something in each of the poets I translated that perhaps echoes a lyric current in my own work, or that already existed there inside me. In that way we might also say, for instance, that Primo Levi is somehow an imitator of Ungaretti.

CV: Ungaretti, even without trying, takes the excess away, goes to the marrow, makes words of sea-light and mountain, brings those two big opposites together in the bone of the language.

SY: What means even more to me is that when Ungaretti was in Alexandria he protected workers, sailors in the mutiny. Even in a politics that he didn't like or share, he helped people in trouble. And then importantly he also made a revolution in Italian poetry. We can think of his time in Paris and of the wonderful poem he wrote about the death of his friend, a poem of personal remembrance. As with all great poets, he wrote of harsh realities spoken with a dignity and a sense of truth, as Cristina was saying just before.

SW: One of the first times I heard you read, in your early days in London, you read a poem in memory of Cavafy (SY: "Yes, 'Cavafy's House' ") and you said that you'd translated Cavafy and my heart went out to you. (SY: "At Poetry Café, in Covent Garden?") What a wonderful thing to do! But can you talk a little more about what he meant to you in your work.

SY: I met Cavafy through Auden's famous introduction to the translation. I got to know his poetry, and also his life. When I read Cavafy, what made me even more attached to him was the strict system of language he strived to achieve; the poetic sentence of Cavafy was constructed in a very difficult and strict way. My respect is for that precision. And then again, history becomes day-to-day life in his work, history is life within us . . . Penelope is not a stranger, not part of mythology, she's our contemporary, our neighbour. That is what I call (and he grins wickedly) Cavafy's great satanic power (we all laugh). In Alexandria, 20 years ago or so, there was no Cavafy Museum but there was a room in Lipsius Street, and I said to the doorman there that I wanted to see that old Greek man's room. He said to me: "Oh, people always come to me and ask to see the room and there's nothing in there at all, nothing . . ." So I went to Cavafy's room – and I remember that work room – his mirror was there and his poems, and that balcony, his tiny balcony looking out over the one-way street and it is there he has Mark Anthony . . . "The God Forsakes Anthony" . . . that great poem . . . on that tiny balcony. (Laughs) So every time I went to Alexandria I used to visit that room, but then the Greek Consulate changed things; they tidied up the room and it lost its originality. Ferial Ghazoul, who was working in Cairo at the time, wrote an essay "Cavafy and the Iraqi Poet Sa'di Yusuf" linking my poems "Cavafy's House" and "Ithaca Trees" to Cavafy's work, to his poems "Ithaca" and "The God Forsakes Anthony". She talks about that room in the essay.

SW: I love the way that you name people and poets and places throughout your poetry. In titles and throughout the bodies of poems, so many of them are dated by place or celebrate places close to you. Not a lot of poets bother to do that or do it so naturally . . .

SY: Space, names, places, persons are flesh to the text. It's a kind of documentation. From its origins poetry has had the voyager principle embedded in it. For example, Homer is very important; we have to respect the man as he taught us how to respect space, people, place, names in poetry, map-making; he was a great teacher. In a way we are near each other and we go together. We carry on learning. Or we learn from Ritsos. Or Lorca. You know Lorca once said, when he was asked whether he supported the Republican or Falangist cause, he answered: "I am with the loser." Poets are with the losers. Even in politics the poet is with the loser, always. With the marginalised and we defend . . . Against power . . . We are the losers still. (*We all laugh.*) And we are laughers! (*And we laugh some more.*)

SW: And now you are cast up on these shores on the edge of London . . .

SY: That's right, stranded here by the shore (laughs). One time I lost my bankcard, or it didn't work, on the shores of Canada, with Iqbal. And I was laughing but also shouting "I am stranded by the Canadian shore. Please call London". That's precisely what I said and I received a telephone call back from London to sort it out. So, I am stranded here on the edge of London now, but in a paradise of

DIGITAL BANIPAL

– the more than ever open window on contemporary Arab literature

Now Banipal is even more open, with the digital edition offering readers all over the world the chance to flip open the magazine on their computers, iPads, iPhones or androids, wherever they are, search through the issues and sync them.

All for £18 a year (3 issues). A digital subscription comes with full access to back issues going back to *Banipal 31*, Spring 2008, with more being added. In 2015, all back issues will have been digitised, and a combined print+digital subscription will be available – for both individuals and institutions. Until then the print and online subscriptions are separate.

Free iTunes App. Preview the current issue or check out the Free Trial issue – *Banipal 40 – Libyan Fiction*

For more information, go to: www.banipal.co.uk/subscribe/

Banipal's digital partner   EXACT EDITIONS

trees and lakes and good air, with the good health of walking and exercise. I am close to water again as I was in my childhood, so I like this place.

When I first came here it gave me the security that is needed to write. And when I first came here I wrote almost daily, feeling the breath of air – and that was good. But more recently I have become tired and I need a change. I want to start writing in a different way, and this takes time and thinking. Now I am a well-known poet, at least in the Arab world. But after these seven volumes [of the *Collected Poetical Works*] have been published.[8] I feel I must write in a new way, I must make a new start. I've been thinking about this for months now. I'm trying to write in a more "structural" way, in a more sophisticated way, with greater interchange of time and events. And including silence also. All this is not an issue with shorter poems; they can just be written down. But this will be a book poem. It will need some planning and I think that perhaps in a month's time I will be able to begin writing.

CV: Perhaps as we age we gain longer sight and wider "breath" and in a short poem you don't have those same choices to form words in your heart.

SY: Yes, yes . . .

SW: I was going to ask you, echoing one of your early poems: "Saadi, my reasonable sir, what are you writing tonight?" – or in a month's time – but you have just told us! (Laughter)

SY: Well, I have to start it. And it will be a more autobiographical piece, with details, going back to try to go forward. I am thinking about it, about a book poem.

SW: I haven't asked you much about the question of freedom, and freedom is something you have always held very close to you, and struggled for. About personal freedoms in poetry, and political freedoms in people. Also I've not asked yet you about other Arab poets and I would really like you to talk about Badr Shakir al-Sayyab.

SY: It's quite important for me to talk about Badr because we are from the same village near Basra, and I met him very early on. Especially, I remember in 1949 – although I first met him before then – but in 1949 I was a member of the Iraqi Communist Party and at that time it seemed to be having something of a revival. I had a message that someone was trying to reconnect with me so I went to meet him and it was Badr. After that we kept in contact. In 1964 he was in Basra Port Hospital and I was just out of prison; I went to visit him every day. One day I told him I was leaving the country. He was taken to Kuwait and I went to Algeria, and he died.

I think that in artistic terms the questions he asked in poetry have still not been answered till now – in language, in music, dealing with history, dealing with heritage, and I mean the heritage of poetry.

Until now there are no answers. I think he has ten poems that are among the very best and most pure of all Arabic poetry. It's not easy to write ten such poems. Rilke talked about ten verses. But

Stephen Watts and Saadi Youssef outside Saadi's home

ten poems! I learnt very much from him. So maybe I will try to go back to the same environment of his work. Some critics think he was too rural, not of the city, but he was; they were wrong. In the villages near Basra there was great influence from the Left, more so than in Basra itself. There was greater organisation of strikes and workers' activity. There was a Sufi *tekke*, centre, in the neighbourhood and the sons of the sheikh were all Communists – I met the youngest son of the sheikh in Poland. He has a café there. (*Laughs*) So he, and Badr, had a far greater understanding of urban politics and of workers' realities than those critics maintain.

SW: And what of the younger generations, the more contemporary writers?

SY: I prefer not to talk about this. Nowadays I am in touch with the younger generation of writers and artists, but in general there is nothing serious now in art or writing. Iraq has a damaged culture, it is a damaged country. There is a kind of what I call "bullet in the back of your neck" censorship. It's very dangerous to write now. Tens of thousands of people are fleeing the country, terrible things are happening everywhere. But there's nothing in writing. A minimum condition of basic security is needed for good writing, and that just isn't there for now.

Notes:

1 "Shatt al-Arab" poem, translated by Khaled Mattawa, is posted on *The Blue Moon* review website.
2 "Imru al-Qais's Grandson" is published in *Nostalgia, My Enemy*, translated by Sinan Antoon and Peter Money
3 "Genesis '34" was translated by Sinan Antoon and can be read on the webpage: www.jadaliyya.com
4 "AMERICA, AMERICA" is translated by Khaled Mattawa, first published in *Banipal* 7 (2000), then in the collection *Without An Alphabet, Without A Face* (Graywolf Press, 2002. It can be read online at http://www.poemhunter.com/poem/america-america-11/ along with other poems of Saadi Youssef translated by Khaled.
5 "Post Cards from Hajj Omrane" was translated by Fawaz Trabulsi, and can be read on http://www.jehat.com/Jehaat/en/Poets/SaadiYoussef1.htm
6 "Thank You Imru ul-Qais" is translated by Khaled Mattawa, published in *Without An Alphabet, Without A Face* and can be read on www.poethunter.com at http://www.poemhunter.com/poem/thank-you-imru-ul-qais/
7 Listen to Saadi Youssef reading "Cafavy's House", and other poems, recorded in 2009 for the "Between Two Worlds: Poetry and Translation" project at the British Library on http://sounds.bl.uk/Arts-literature-and-performance/Between-two-worlds-poetry-and-translation/024M-C1340X0017XX-0000V0
8 Saadi is being rather self-deprecating here: for many years he's been revered as a poet through the Arab world and beyond. And in June 2014, his *Collected Poetical Works,* in a set of seven large volumes, as he mentions above, was published in Beirut.

SALIH J ALTOMA

Recollections about Sa'di Yusuf's College Experience

The white windows and the door
You opened them, and the forest swayed,
The flowers in their garden began to question
Your mad longing
Say to your flowers what a dreamer would say:
The lover has arrived and my family is out
Say it . . . your flowers won't reveal it
Flowers and lovers are intimately bound.

Sa'di Yusuf, 1952

I

I consider it a great pleasure to take part in this celebration of Sa'di Yusuf's 80th birthday. I do so, first, because of my profound respect for his outstanding achievements as a poet, essayist and translator whose career I have followed for more than 50 years. I do so also because this celebration reminds me of Baghdad's happier days and the city's promising cultural trends, which Sa'di and I, and other Iraqis of our generation shared in the mid-20th century.

Sa'di and I were then pursuing our studies at the famed Iraqi College, Dar al-Mu'allimin al-Aliyah (the Higher Teachers College), where Iraq's leading modernist poets such as Nazik al-Mala'ika, Badr Shakir al-Sayyab, Abd al-Wahhab al-Bayati and Shadhil Taqah received their education. I refer specifically to the time we shared as students majoring in Arabic: 1950-1952 (myself in the years 1948-1952 and Sa'di from 1950-1954). Numerous Western studies dealing with Sa'di often refer to his college background but they rarely, if ever, offer any specific link between this background and his emergence as a poet. Yair Huri's excellent study *The Poetry of Sa'di Yusuf: Between Homeland and Exile*, for example, refers to it only once as "the renowned Higher Teachers' Training Institute". Many other similar passing references can be found in recent studies on contemporary Iraqi poets who received their education at the Higher Teachers College.

In contrast to this gap in Western studies, there has lately been a growing corpus in Arabic about our college's historical role in producing, from its foundation, prominent figures in different fields:

poetry, fiction, drama, politics, education and criticism. Aptly called "*Masna' al-intalijinsia al-iraqiyyah al-wa'iyah*" (Mill/Factory of the enlightened Iraqi intelligentsia) it has been recognized as the institution associated with (if not the birthplace of) the free verse movement that was spearheaded by al-Mala'ika and al-Sayyab (in 1947/1948). It is regrettable to note, however, that pertinent studies in Western languages are still lacking, with the exception of an MA thesis submitted to the American University in Beirut in 1963 under the title *The Higher Teachers College, Baghdad: A History, 1923-1958.**

II

To briefly outline the College's impact on Sa'di's early development as a poet, it is important, I believe, to describe both the general atmosphere prevailing at the time and the course of study Sa'di and others were required to follow.

In one of his early interviews (1979) Sa'di acknowledged the positive impact the cultural climate had on his decision to seriously pursue poetry as a career. He has also said, in another: "I went to study at the University of Baghdad in the mid-1950s. Cultural life in Iraq was rich then."

But in both instances, he offered no specific details regarding the richness of the cultural atmosphere at the college or cultural life in Iraq in general.

As several recent accounts by Iraqi writers have repeatedly emphasized, the post Second World War years in Baghdad witnessed the flowering of modernist trends and literature which were reflected in the works of numerous rising artists, poets and short story writers (such as Jawad Salim, Faiq Hasan, Khalid al-Rahhal, Nazik al-Mala'ika, Badr Shakir al-Sayyab, Abd al-Wahhab al-Bayati, and Abd al-Malik Nuri). To quote Wisam al-Zahawi from his essay "The Cultural Scene in Baghdad and its Socio-Political Backdrop in the Fifties: A Memoir":

> Plays, professional and amateur, were staged, concerts and recitals were well-attended. Art exhibitions were mounted in various venues. Television was introduced to Iraq in 1954; the cultural activities were often televised, gaining a much wider audience.

In another informative essay by Khaled Al-Sultany entitled "Half a century after the creation of the 'Wright' projects in Baghdad: Plans for the imagined architecture", the period is characterized as "the most radiant, powerful and important years in Iraq's modern history". Sultany goes on to maintain that "the nineteen fifties had a special flavour and a specific importance, enhanced by the fact that nothing in Iraq's modern history has equalled what was achieved in that time: neither before the decade nor after it".

Based on my personal recollection, I believe that Sa'di had in mind not only the general scene in Baghdad at that time but perhaps more directly the college's unique climate which had enriched students' lives and served to broaden their horizons. Writing recently of their days at the college, former students seem to be unanimous in their positive assessment of its impact on their lives and careers.

This was due to several factors. First, because of its admission policy based on selecting students from all provinces, the college was known for its emphasis on national representation of Iraq. As a result of such a policy, students had the opportunity to interact for the first time, in one place and for four years, with fellow Iraqis who were representative of Iraq in terms of their religious, ethnic, sectarian and political affiliations. In a sense this foresighted practice provided students with an opportunity to break away from their narrow local backgrounds, to think of a shared national identity and to develop reciprocal friendships and understanding beyond their own backgrounds.

As a co-educational school, it offered students of both sexes, again for the first time, an enriching experiment and experience in living and studying on the same campus. It was inevitable that those as-piring to become poets would find in such a mixed environment an appealing and irresistible source of inspiration. That's why poets like Badr Shakir al-Sayyab, Sa'di Yusuf, Abd al-Razzaq Abd al-Wahid, Shadhil Taqah and many others (before and after them) showed a marked preoccupation with themes of love, which often revolved around an unrequited love. As an example, I still remember Sa'di reciting in a calm, soft tone, in 1952 a poem that continued to res-onate in my mind, for its beauty and daring public invitation to love in a co-educational setting. Written in the conventional two-hemistich form, it begins with the following lines:

...

The white windows and the door
You opened them, and the forest swayed,
The flowers in their garden began to question
Your mad longing
Say to your flowers what a dreamer would say:
The lover has arrived and my family is out
Say it . . . your flowers won't reveal it
Flowers and lovers are intimately bound.

Other factors which enriched students' lives and experiences in-cluded frequent poetry readings, which usually culminated in an annual poetry festival, periodic theatrical performances based on Arabic and translated foreign plays, and exhibitions of students' paintings, which reflected at the time new trends in Iraqi art. The latter are of particular significance in view of the fact that leading Iraqi artists including Jawad Salim (1920-1961) served at the college as artists-in-residence, as advisors to guide students (majoring in Arabic or other areas) interested in painting and sculpture. [Among such students, I wish to cite as an example the noted painter Naziha Rashid (al-Harithi), a classmate, who began her training under Jawad Salim's guidance while pursuing her specialization in Arabic (1948-1952).]

Finally, reference should be made to the active participation of many students in political activities, demonstrations, strikes, and other forms of protest in opposition to government policies or in support of Arab and international causes. Student involvement was not without risk of arrest or expulsion (Abd al-Razzaq Abd al-Wahid was expelled for a whole year and Badr Shakir al-Sayyab was like-wise expelled and jailed), but they were encouraged by promising signs: free press, free elections, and a secular multiple party system under which five different parties operated legally at that time. There were in addition other underground movements, including the Iraqi Communist Party (ICP) which was then perhaps most vis-ible and influential among college students. I was well aware, for example, of the fact that Sa'di Yusuf and our mutual friend Abd al-Razzaq Abd al-Wahid (my classmate for four years) were associated with the ICP and that they had communist leanings, but the question of their membership was never raised or stated publicly. In his recent memoirs, Abd al-Razzaq seems to confirm that he and Sa'di were cell members before they joined the party during their student years, though Sa'di, according to Abd al-Razzaq had some reservations at first and was reluctant to be an active member.

III

As far as the course of study was concerned, it consisted of several components: Arabic – the core subject, English and French, history, and educational courses intended to train students to become high school teachers.

Undoubtedly it was the Arabic component that provided us with a four-year intensive study of Arabic literature and grammar. It was a truly rigorous and demanding program for an obvious reason: to prepare teachers qualified to teach Classical Arabic, the formal (fusha) variety. Divided into segments, the program covered in chronological order the various periods: the Pre-Islamic (first year), the Qur'an, early Islamic and Umayyad (second year), the Abbasid (third year) and the Andalusian (fourth year). This was in addition to the study of Arabic grammar, prosody and rhetoric. We were fortunate to have had as mentors eminent literary historians, grammarians and philologists, such as Muhammad Mahdi al-Basir (1895-1974) known as the poet of the 1920 revolt against the British occupation, Mustafa Jawad (1904-1969), Ahmad Abd al-Sattar al-Jawari (1924-1988), Salim al-Nu'aymi (1911-1984) and Abd al-Razzaq Muhyi al-Din (1910-1983). All were noted not only for their scholarly publications, some of which we studied, but also for the encouragement and personal interest they displayed regarding students' literary talents.

Sa'di, for example, acknowledged (in his 1979 interview) that he received feedback from his mentor Muhyi al-Din, who seems to have shown a special interest in Sa'di's poems while he was attending the college. Muhyi al-Din, a noted poet himself, was known for his strict conformity to the classical tradition of the two-hemistich form. He was vehemently opposed to the emerging free verse movement, and continued his harsh criticism in some of his writings, including a paper he presented to the Arabic Language Academy in Cairo in 1976. Knowing that Sa'di adhered to the conventional form in his early poetry until 1955 (i.e., after his graduation), I am inclined to believe that his hesitation in using the free verse form was due primarily to Muhyi al-Din's outlook and guidance. He may have been influenced by other teachers, who were also noted for their negative views of the free verse movement at that time. But Sa'di's adherence to the conventional form did not last long; he decided to distance himself almost completely from it after his graduation. Indeed, in his 1979 interview, Sa'di even went as far as to declare that he could not stand the conventional form in the 20th century and viewed it as "anti-history" (mu'adiyah li al-tarikh), according to the interview. This is in spite of the fact that he always expressed his reverence and admiration for its role in classical Arabic heritage. It is instructive to note, however, that the conventional form continues to demonstrate its vitality and great appeal to large audiences, as it is used effectively by numerous poets, including Abd al-Razzaq Abd al-Wahid.

The Arabic course of study had other components, including two that are relevant to Sa'di's literary career: the study of foreign languages (two years of English and four years of French) and the course on Ancient History. The language courses were intended to ensure that students would acquire basic proficiency primarily for reading purposes. It is difficult to speak about the extent of students' success in achieving the required level of competence. I am not aware of any study that can shed light on this issue. But it is safe to assume that English and French courses served Sa'di in his literary career as a poet eager for direct interaction with international poetry and as a translator who demonstrated his distinction in translating numerous works. As his record indicates, Sa'di stands out as one of the most productive Arab poets by virtue of his dedicated efforts to enrich Arabic with literary works from other languages. According to an interview (Banipal 20, Summer 2004), he was able in the 1950s to read in English American short stories by Hemingway and others "which had a great impact on him". "I learned how to be honest towards daily life," Sa'di noted, "how I could stand against exaggeration, how my language could be more democratic, I mean, more the language of every-day usage." I may add that in another interview for PEN World Voices, Sa'di refers only to French as the language he studied at the college but cites English as the first foreign language, which he learned at primary school:

WRR: What was the first language you learned after Arabic? SY: Well, English in primary school. In university I started learning French, and then I lived in Algeria for more than seven years where I used French daily. Then I went to France. I was in Paris for three years so my French became more polished.

See http://www.wildriverreview.com/PEN-World-Voices/interview/saadi-youssef/tonight-we-rest-here/stocke

The component concerned with Ancient History was taught by Taha Baqir (1912-1984), one of Iraq's most distinguished archeologists and ancient historians. I single out this subject not because other periods of Arab-Islamic history which we studied were not important for our education, but because it may have contributed to the increased use of Mesopotamian myths in contemporary Iraqi literature: poetry, fiction and drama. The latter is often attributed to James George Frazer's *The Golden Bough*, which was partly translated into Arabic by Jabra Ibrahim Jabra during his years as a lecturer in the English department at the college (1948-1952). Jabra published the first two chapters of his translation in Baghdad in 1954 (in *al-Fusul al-Arab'ah*), a journal edited by Buland al-Haydari, before publishing his translation in Beirut in 1957. There is no doubt about the impact that Jabra's translation had on al-Sayyab in particular, and on other Iraqi poets. But the course on ancient Iraqi history and literature should not be overlooked as a source for the proliferation of mythological figures or events such as Dumuzi (Tammuz), Gilgamesh, Ishtar and others. It is known that Taha Baqir taught the subject to generations of students from the early 1940s until 1963. In addition, he was at that time working on the *Epic of Gilgamesh* and was involved in translating parts of it. Baqir's first translation in co-operation with his colleague Fu'ad Safar was published in 1950, but more detailed versions of his translation appeared in several editions before and after his death – in 1962, 1971, 1975, 1986, 1988, and 2002.

In brief, I believe, in the light of what I have outlined above, that Sa'di's academic experience at the college, and his prolonged and intensive interaction with major poets and writers of the classical period, provided him with a solid foundation. This, combined with his talent and dedication, enabled Sa'di to pursue a rarely matched distinguished literary career not only as a great poet, but also as a prose writer whose style is comparable to the finest in modern and classical Arabic writing.**

Notes:
(*) The thesis was written by Niam Khalid El-Hashimi, (d. 2008 in London) a former trustee of the British Arab Resource Centre, and the daughter of one of the college deans, Dr. Khalid al-Hashimi. A well-documented study, not yet published, it provides a detailed historical survey of the college's evolution from its foundation in 1923 until 1958. I believe it can serve as a basis for other studies regarding the college's leading alumni and their place in Iraq's modern history. I wish to acknowledge my debt to the library of the American University in Beirut for sending me a copy of this thesis.

(**) My recollections regarding Sa'di's literary career are not confined to our shared college years but include also my attempts to follow from distance his writings since the 1960s. I began my residence in the United States in 1960 and sadly never had a chance to meet Sa'di again, though we maintained our correspondence periodically. I had occasions to refer to his works in both Arabic and English publications. My earlier references were to Sa'di's skillful incorporation into his poetry of Iraqi folkloric songs and phrases (See *al-Muthaqqaf*, 1960) and to his unique style in comparison to other Iraqi poets, as can be seen from the following passage published in *World Literature Today* (1972):

> In contrast to the broad preoccupations of the preceding poets, (Nazik al-Mala'ika, Badr al-Sayyab, Abd al-Wahhab al-Bayati) Sa'di Yusuf stands out fairly unique in his devotion to localized themes, particularly those pertaining to the life of the common man, Iraq's southern landscape and his native city, Basra. Furthermore he has been more successful than others in his attempt to develop a conversational poetic idiom through frequent blending of Iraqi colloquial phrases, songs, and proverbs with the traditional literary language. Examples of these characteristics are especially notable in his "Visible Poems" (1965), which includes many poems from an earlier work, *51 Poems* (1959), but can be found in other collections he has published: *The Pirate* (1952), *Songs Not for Others* (1954), *The Star and the Ashes* (1961), and *Far From the First Sky* (1970). (See "Postwar Iraqi Literature: Agonies of Rebirth" *Books Abroad* (=*World Literature Today*) 46.2 (Spring, 1972 : 211-217).

Other personal efforts include a few translations of Sa'di's poetry (such as AMERICA AMERICA, *alJadid*, September 1997) and bibliographical coverage of English translation of his writings, which appeared in several books and journals including *Iraq's Modern Arabic Literature: A Guide to English Translations since 1950* (2010).

RAWI HAGE

POEM FOR SAADI

BIOGRAPHY

Uncompromising nails
hanging in exile's cups
oceans in violet liquid
guessing the horizon's destruction
Colonies of birds in metal covers
you tore my Babylonian sky

I have prophesied your coming
while the Bedouins cheered
the Khamseen's arrival
two stars above schools
of finger licking fish
splitting the Tigris river

Saadi, they heard your prophesies
against their own mirrors
Forgetful fluid
Complacent dust
Hunchbacked animals
blinded by a hundred names
Wind
storm
pass
in conquest
You knew them better than their prophets

KHALIL SUWAILIH

The Eternal Exile

Saadi Youssef's position with regard to the Arab Spring placed him in the line of fire. But instead of looking closely at the reasons behind his position, many who supported the revolutions have chosen to throw out his entire literary legacy. Emerging from the alleyways of Facebook, many sought to defame him and call him a traitor. It would not have been difficult for Saadi Youssef to cross to the other side, to wave a flag, chant along with the others and have pictures of himself snapped in the main squares. Instead, he verbalized his doubts about the flowering of the bloody Spring, accusing America of being behind it.

Saadi Youssef never defended tyrants for the sake of bags of dinars and instead chose the path of exile. He was the one who made "Waiting for the Barbarians" by Cavafy available in Arabic, through his translation, as well as poems by Lorca, Walt Whitman, Ritsos, and others. He has been like a gardener who has pruned Arabic poetry of its weeds and redundant echoes.

We need to remember him in his khaki fatigues returning to Damascus from Beirut after the Israeli invasion in 1982. We need to put aside his emotional pronouncements and re-read poems like "Maryam comes"*, which he wrote under bombardment, or appreciate the amazing lucidity one sees in "The Ends of the African North"*. We should be celebrating the publication of his whole works as befitting his lifetime achievement, without grudges or misgivings.

* Both these poems are translated by Khaled Mattawa and published in *Without an Alphabet, Without a Face*. "Maryam comes" is also online at http://weekly.ahram.org.eg/2006/804/cu4.htm.

The Arab intellectual works with the politics that is financially lucrative and avoids the politics that requires sacrifice, struggle and prison. In my opinion, we have now a critical theatre, which I call "flirtation" and which stands against the involvement of any creative person in critical issues. It is a theatre which tells you that art has no connection to politics or with social issues.

From an interview with Saadi Youssef
in *Al-Akhbar* newspaper, Beirut, 30 August 2014

YAIR HURI

Exile and Imagination in Sa'di's Poetry

"Who builds a capital for the poet if not the poet himself"

Between a home that immures me and a wide sky,
how will I choose my home?
Between my silence and my song,
how will I choose my whisper?
(Sa'di Yusuf, "A Poem")

The interchangeability of home and exile, here and there, memory
and forgetting points to the fact that all concepts of origin and be-
longing — whether real or invented — that one venerates are mere
fictions that one can construct as well as deconstruct.
(Mustapha Hamil, "Exile and its Discontents")

The experience of exile and displacement has been an essential generative force for artists and writers throughout the 20th Century, and arguably long before. Whether the exile is forced or voluntary, the convergence of expatriation with the experience of creativity has been an ongoing force in artistic and literary vanguardism. Exiled artists and writers throughout history have refigured and reimagined both aesthetic and geographic boundaries, and their work has often been radical, shaping changes beyond the aesthetic or formal. In this sense, by relocating themselves to different cultures, exiles inevitably give birth to more universal ideas, the result of the integration of the local mind with the universal cognitive map. Poets and writers, displaced by force or choice, have produced the type of work that shatters boundaries, perhaps mirroring the ruptures evident in their changed geographies, allowing them what Julia Kristeva has called "exquisite distance."

Sa'di Yusuf, Iraq's foremost living poet, has long been acknowledged as one of the progenitors of "the exilic poem" in modern Arabic literature. One cannot fail to observe the astuteness of his insights as well as the poetic power in his mapping of the stages of an exile's transformation in and adaptation to exile. Although many Arab poets and writers have been exiled or have chosen expatriation or emigration, no other poet has so deeply engaged with exile as a subject and explored so obsessively the role of dispersion and fragmentation in his poetic works as Yusuf did.

Saadi Youssef in Jam'a el-Fna in Marrakech, photo by Samuel Shimon

In his seminal essay "The Writer in Exile or the Literature of Exile and Counter-Exile", literary critic Claudio Guillén distinguishes between two types of narratives of exile. In the first, "exile becomes its own subject matter", and it often belongs to the elegiac mode. This kind of writing reveals a tendency towards "a direct expression of sorrow" and it is usually submerged by the hardships of displacement. In the second, "exile is the condition but not the visible cause of an imaginative response often characterized by a tendency toward integration, increasingly broad vistas or universalism" (Guillén, 1976: 272). He calls the latter kind a literature of "counter-exile," in which authors "incorporate the separation from place, class, language, or native community, insofar as they triumph over the separation and thus offer wide dimensions of meanings and transcend the earlier attachment to place or native origin" (Ibid., ibid). In this kind of narrative, Guillén claims, the writer tries to put the expulsion into perspective in a balanced and meaningful way and attempts to overcome – but not forget – the tragedy of exile. The "literature of exile," according to Guillén, is linked to "modern feelings of nationalism" whereas in the "literature of counter-exile," so Guillén argues, "no great writer can remain a merely local mind, unwilling to question the relevance of the particular place from which he writes." (Ibid.: 275, 280) Indeed, in the latter kind of narrative, exile is almost stripped of its "tragic edge" and becomes an elixir of freedom from the suffocating grip of national identity.

I contend that whereas Yusuf's exilic writings until 1982 clearly belong to the first kind, those dating after his departure from Yemen belong to the second. Yusuf's later exilic writings do not address exile itself, but rather exemplify a type of narrative written in exile. His poems evince the exilic sensibility even though the poet by and large shuns the clear and direct thematization of exile. The theme of exile thus becomes an undercurrent in the later poetry of Yusuf, and only occasionally surfaces in an expansive singular image. In an existentialist mode, Yusuf iterates the poet's quest for self-identity within a vastly changing cultural configuration. Past and present historical moments interweave, unveiling persistent themes of displacement, cultural syncretism, and the search for identity. Thus, the poetics that Yusuf actuates seeks to supersede and transcend the rhetoric of binary oppositions that have traditionally evaluated exile in opposition to the homeland. Exile has become for Yusuf the crucible in which he is able to examine questions of deracination, cultural dislocation, homesickness for an elusive home, the search for a new sense of identity, the pain of loss or dispossession, and, ultimately, the reconfiguration of her identity and reintegration.

What constitutes the true originality in Yusuf's exilic output is the combined sensation of strangeness and at-homeness which the poems create. Talking about his situation as an artist in extended exile, Yusuf formulates the core of his creativity:

[In exile, the poet] either shows fidelity to his heritage and his native land or, when time goes by, takes his material from the "other land" he lives in. That is, he is no longer dependent upon remembrance and longing, (Yusuf, 2003: 14):

I think of myself now as a poet who is a resident of the world. I don't feel exiled. Being outside my country has become my ordinary life. I am used to it. I feel at home wherever I am [. . .] I have to establish real contact with the country I am in, with the people and

> with the environment. I have to grasp daily life in its details and
> minutiae. That is how I write poetry. The details and minutiae are
> my raw material. I am not conditioning myself to do that; it is di-
> rect, honest contact with people, culture, with nature. It is a kind
> of open receptivity to the world, to the universe.
>   (Yusuf, 2004, 8-9)

Yusuf's exile poetry does in fact start from a radical openness to the outer world, an openness which carries its own special danger. The poet is aware that refusing to incur that peril is tantamount to succumbing to mediocre versifying, since lyrical expression requires the hard-won and easily lost determination that Paul Tillich called "the courage to be". The later poems are rich with geographical and literary texture, which supports and gives body to the meditation that forms the main strand of the poem. These poems allow him to negotiate between his often idiosyncratic local observations, auto-biographical moments and putatively universal philosophical claims. Clearly Yusuf's approach undermines claims by other exiled artists to a natural connection between strong cultural identity and geographic location. His later approach deconstructs the semantic unit identity-place, and asserts that writers can also be "at home" when living in different, changing physical surroundings. In this context, the theoretical distinction made between place and space is helpful (Gupta & Ferguson, 1992: 6-23; Giddens 1991). Place has been de-fined as the actual locality where people live, or in other words, as the material surroundings through which they physically move dur-ing their daily routine. Space, by contrast, is "the general idea peo-ple have of where things should be in physical and cultural relation to each other." Hastings & Thomas, 1999: 9) In other words, space is a mental picture instead of particular locality.

Finally, Yusuf speaks of the imagination as the most intensive province of pleasure and pain and defines it as a creative power of the mind, representing the images of things in the order and manner in which they were received by the senses or in combining them in a new manner and according to a different order. Yusuf's poem "Ila Hashim Shafiq" (To Hashim Shafiq) splendidly asserts his confidence in the poetic act and in the rehabilitating power of the mind against the encroaching nature of exile:

ستكون "بلد"
يوماً، عاصمة الدنيا . . .
وستبني أنتَ
– أنت الذاهل في مدن الغيتو
ساحاتٍ
وبساتينَ
وأكواخًا من سعف وجذوعٍ
وستسكنها
لتكونَ، ولو نبتتْ في أوراق الدفتر،
عاصمة الدنيا.

. . .

من يبني عاصمةً للشاعر
غير الشاعر

> You will be "a city"
> one day, the capital of the world . . .
> you will build
> — you, the befuddled who wanders in the cities of ghettos —
> squares,
> gardens
> and huts made out of palm fronds and trunks.
> You will inhabit it
> and become, if only inside the leaves of a notebook,
> the capital of the world.
> . . .
> Who builds a capital for the poet
> if not the poet himself?

Indeed, that is pretty well exactly what Seamus Heaney means by "redress" when he discusses the purpose of poetry; it is "the imagination pressing back against the pressure of reality" (Heaney, 1995: I):

In the activity of poetry too, there is a tendency to place counter-reality in the scales — a reality which may be only imagined but which nevertheless has weight because it is imagined within the gravitational pull of the actual and can therefore hold its own and balance out against the historical situation. This redressing effect of poetry comes from its being a glimpsed alternative, a revelation of potential that is denied or threatened by circumstances [. . .] The creative spirit remains positively recalcitrant in face of the negative evidence, reminding the indicative mood of history that it has been written in by force and written in over the good optative mood of human potential. (Ibid, 3, 24)

References

• Guillén, Claudio. (1976). "The Writer in Exile or the Literature of Exile and Counter-Exile," in *Books Abroad* 50: 271-80.
• Gupta Akhil. & Ferguson James. (1992) "Beyond 'Culture': Space. Identity and the Politics of Difference," in *Cultural Anthropology* 7, 1: 6–23.
• Giddens, Anthony. (1991). *Modernity and Self-Identity*. Cambridge: Polity Press.
• Hastings, Donnan & Wilson, Thomas. (1999). *Borders: Frontiers of Identity, Nation and State*. Oxford & New York.
• Heaney, Seamus. (1995). The Redress of Poetry. London: Faber & Faber.
• Yusuf , Sa'di. (1995). *Al-A'mal al-Kamila*. Damascus: D r al-Mada.
• --------------. (2003). "Interview with Sa'di Yusuf," in *Al-Watan* 21 August: 13-18.
• --------------. (2004). "I Have Trained Myself Hard to be Free," in *Banipal* 20: 2-14.

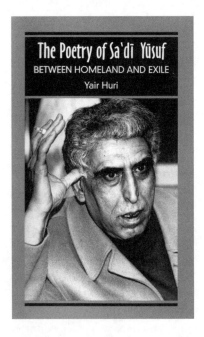

Yair Huri's work *The Poetry of Sa'di Yusuf: Between Homeland and Exile* is published by Sussex Academic Press
ISBN: 978-1845191481,352pp, Hbk.
http://www.sussex-academic.com/sa/titles/literary_criticism/huri.htm

HASSAN NAJMI

With Saadi Youssef at the foot of a mural in Tangier

TRANSLATED BY CAMILO GOMEZ-RIVAS

Nada se puede hacer
Soy otro
y soy el mismo
    Efraín Bartolomé

Like a gull looking down on the waves of Tangier
like a saint born of the dust of exile, of travel and of words,
landing in the lobby of the hotel, his arms raised banners of
   glory
his left hand waving to strike out neutrals
his right recalling his youth over a succession of wrinkles
his yesterday has led to Tangier's drizzly morning
the glass of wine washes his ringing laughter

On the way to El Dorado (I mean the restaurant), to La
Grenouille (I mean the bar), he slackens his pace. In its look and
in its verdure, his tree is alone and spreads its shade like a forest.
He slackens in the glass, in despair. He beats pure spirit – the
beating of the clocks in his heart (unadulterated, fearless).

Such is the poet; have a good look –

You can see him, pure like a white night, calm as a poem of soft cadence (did he write it for himself?) You can say he's become someone else. You will see how he brings bits of bread to scatter where the birds can find them. How he rescues a butterfly with broken wings. He has that thirst for a relentless red god. You will see how he greets the retired sailors, the bartender, the parking attendant. How he fills the empty space with his gesticulations, turning to the decayed buildings of Tangier, to the stones crumbling in the alley. How he is regretful over a Moroccan woman, essence of basil disintegrating. To the Tangier night, light-winged, falling.

In Tangier I see the poet. I see him place the meaning outside the tongue.

(Here near the tongue, in image, in people).

I see him light-heeled on the pavement – wrapped in a halo of silence like a butterfly planting its shadow in the ground. He drinks his red milk in Tangier and sees Iraq in the glass. He sees Iraq in every palm stripped of shadow. In the summers crackling in the provinces. In every fogged-up glass. In the wind going, in the soft breeze coming. In the poem –

in every poem he sees an Iraq of palms desiccated by uranium
(The poet has no capacity for neglect –
the poem has no capacity for forgetfulness).

He will see Iraq in every morning train
in every late whistle
in every rail that takes him back to first love, to first prison
to memories of comrades and his shackled wrist
(If only joy could remember!)
In Tangier – at the Ritz, the hotel with the shadow on the side –

Hassan Najmi and Saadi Youssef in west London, 2001, photo by Samuel Shimon

I take my leave of the poet, the sun of Iraq in his touch
I say goodbye to the poet, radiant in his youthful cap and T-shirt
with that soaring look, like an eagle peering through the clouds
that glance that ignites the eyelids of the horizon –
(How many books in his head – how many poems and dreams,
exiles and losses!
How many lives!)
Such is Saadi, he is himself, he alone
(like the stones of the torrent when it gets up to go)
he will entrust nothing – the road will always bring him back to
Tangier
Be kind to Tangier and to the poem until he returns.

SALAH AWWAD

What do you see, Saadi?

Walt Whitman begins his poem "Salut au Monde!" with a line that links the exotic with the familiar. "O take my hand, Walt Whitman" is a prefatory phrase that not only welcomes the world, but existence and self. But his journey of exploration is not over. He asks: "What do you hear, Walt Whitman?" and "What do you see, Walt Whitman?"

Most of those who study Whitman agree that the Old Testament was the base for building his poems. Similarly, Saadi reveals his sources to include Whitman, Cavafy and Ritsos. At the invitation of Salman Rushdie, Saadi attended the 2007 PEN World Voices Festival, ready to search for Whitman in the very city where Whitman crossed daily from Brooklyn to the island of Manhattan.

I accompanied Saadi to the poetry opening event. We took the bus from the hotel and sat directly behind the driver. Surprisingly, Saadi chose a prose piece, "Another Paris Night", and he reviewed it with me on the way there. The hall at Hunter College was packed, and we saw a long line of people waiting to buy tickets to listen to literary voices from all over the world.

We went in through a side entrance and were met by Salman Rushdie. Each participant was limited to twenty minutes. Saadi chose to read his piece in English, which acquired a distinctive melody when he extended the vowels as if he were reading an Arabic text. He was in his own universe; it was as if he was writing a new poetic text.

Once the evening was over, Saadi's senses woke up to the city around him. He wanted to discover it, to roam through it precisely because of its relationship to Whitman. And in the summer of that

Saadi Youssef in Washington Square, NYC, photo by Andrea Tierney

year, Saadi would return to New York to stay a full month. We walked around the city, its restaurants and bars. Saadi wrote every day, and these pieces, guided by the spirit of Whitman, formed his collection entitled New York Poems. Some poems quoted Whitman directly, such as in "Crossing Brooklyn Bridge", and "A song to the West", while others captured images of what Saadi saw in New York of its people and its streets.

It was as if every poem transformed that seventy-year-old man into a happy child. One day we found an Irish pub in the Village whose interior resembled that of a church, with a lectern that

Salah Awwad and Saadi Youssef in New York, photo by Andrea Tierney

priests use to deliver their sermons. Saadi stepped up, glass in hand,
to deliver a sermon outside time and space. We danced our way out
of the pub; Saadi was transformed into a young man full of life and
emotion, just like his poems.

Another time, Saadi surprised me with a conversation about *Moby
Dick* and Herman Melville, whose house in Nantucket, New York
state, has been turned into a museum. A visitor can enter the room
where this great novel was written and see from the window a
mountain that resembles the shape of a whale. Saadi suggested that
we visit Nantucket and so we stayed in Cape Cod for one night and
were ferried the next day to Nantucket. There Saadi traced a thread
of similarity between Nantucket and Basra, the only port in Iraq associated with the adventures of seamen, fishermen and traders, and
the starting point for the stories of Sindbad the sailor. Nantucket
revived Saadi's memories of his first long poem that revolved
around Sindbad. He felt the need to reconnect to Melville's world
and to the bitter struggle with fate, nature and life.

Saadi is a poet who sees with his senses: he is a poet of possibilities
and of space. The city is ever strongly present in his poems. So, what
do you see, Saadi? So much, of that I am sure, just like Gilgamesh,
who toured the world.

SAADI YOUSSEF

WHITENESS

The pasture is all white flowers
and the road crossing the desolate neighborhood
 (where I live) is white flowers.
The roof of my Scottish neighbor's greenhouse is white
 flowers.
Our own backyard and garden white flowers,
and the stairway to our house is white flowers.
Above my pink shirt are white flowers
and my shoes along the path are covered with white
 flowers.
And on the cars (as if to celebrate the wedding of
 Alexander the Great) are white flowers.
The bar door is covered in white flowers.
And on my head a crown of braided white flowers.
And my Austrian lady-friend makes (in season) a candy
 made of eggs and white flowers.
. . . .
. . . .
. . . .
But my cold bed
is empty of white flowers!

London, 11.05.2012

Translated by Khaled Mattawa
from *Poems of Harefield on the Hill*

Cristina Viti reviews

I giardini dell'oblio
[The Gardens of Oblivion]
by **Saadi Yousef**
Translated, introduced by Fawzi Al Delmi
De Angelis Editore, Italy, 2004.
Pbk, 154pp, ISBN 9 788886 218726

Walk together over this sea

In a beautifully concise introduction, translator Fawzi Al Delmi retraces Saadi Youssef's journey through his many places of exile and in parallel, so to speak, follows his charting of a possible route for a radically new poetics and a new politics of language. Al Delmi, a fellow Iraqi, and poet and painter in his own right, has made his home in Milan for the past forty years, and served for some time as a lecturer in Arabic language and literature while working with major publishers to introduce Italian readers to the work of such poets as Yousef, Adonis, Mahmoud Darwish, Amjad Nasser, Mohamed Bennis, Salah Abd al-Sabur, Abbas Beydoun and Qassim Haddad.

Although this is a relatively small book, Al Delmi amply succeeds in giving a balanced overview of Saadi Yousef's poetry spanning the years 1958-2004, while creating translated poems that read beautifully in his "adoptive" Italian language (thus also strongly – if indirectly – challenging the simplistic notion that translators should only work into their "mother tongues").

In the summer and autumn of 2004 *I giardini dell'oblio* was presented at several important international events, including "Il cammino delle comete" in Pistoia, the five-day Mediterranean festival in Rome where the book was launched, and "Salernopoesia" readings organized by the Casa della Poesia in the Campanian town of Baronissi. In 2005 the book won Saadi Yousef special recognition (previously awarded to Gao Xinjiang, Ismail Kadare, Predrag Matvejevi and Titos Patrikios among others) from the Feronia Literary Award, an "anti-prize" created in 1992 by the late Filippo Bettini's cultural organisation Allegorein and the city of Fiano Romano as an alternative to the usual market-based literary awards, with awards for poetry, fiction, non-fiction and special recognition for a foreign author.

In 2004 Bettini had chosen the poetry of Saadi Yousef to spearhead a ground-breaking series, "Scritture per il Mediterraneo" (Writings for and across the Mediterranean), that he created for the publishing house De Angelis. The series was based on an idea of the Mediterranean not being anchored in locality, rather inspired by the image of a focus of convergence, a sort of cultural commons providing a sense of timeless continuity even as its intrinsic mutability requires constant adaptation to shifting parameters of "belonging". Few poets could be said to embody what Bettini called the "unifying values of a wider and ever-open Mediterranean identity" better than Saadi Yousef.

This very fine book, *I giardini dell'oblio*, therefore, can claim with good reason to have provided Italian readers over the last ten years not only with a brilliant, if long overdue, first introduction to Yousef's poetry but also with the opportunity to inscribe their own sense of self within a much enlarged perspective.

In the book's foreword Bettini coined an intricate, but I think, valid neologism when he wrote of Mediterranean countries not as equidistant but "equi-adjacent" because they are touched, although not strictly delimited by, a sea that should be perceived as a shared matrix of myth, knowledge and experience rather than a boundary line. Perhaps this could be an image to hold dear against the relentless assault of news reports, which, as Al Delmi reminds us, show Iraq exclusively as a place of violence and suffering and risk erasing its place at "the fulcrum of civilization".

Perhaps it is not entirely by coincidence that I find myself writing this in the harbour bar of a small West Ligurian town, reading Saadi's magnificent poems in Italian, marvelling anew at their elemental strength, tenderness and staying power. And if none of us can forget that looking at the Mediterranean while looking back over the past ten years also means staring at the mass grave of so many who died in an attempt to escape hunger and war, so too we can celebrate the courage, passion and knowledge of a poet who dares to invite us to "walk together over this sea".

Three years ago Banipal started promoting wider intercultural dialogue in the magazine by featuring non-Arab, non-Arabic works of literature under the heading "Guest Literature". The successful series has seen writers from Slovenia, Germany and South Korea, also the USA, France, Romania and Vietnam. Here we present six very different Dutch fiction writers, introduced by poet and author Victor Schiferli of the Dutch Foundation for Literature.

VICTOR SCHIFERLI

IN THE DUTCH MOUNTAINS

A Brief Excursion into Fiction from The Netherlands through the works of six fiction writers

In 1981, Cees Nooteboom published a novel with the title *In the Dutch Mountains*. This was something extraordinary, since The Netherlands has more resemblance to the bottom of the sea than to the Swiss alps. We have no mountains, just a handful of hills, and meadows in abundance. (Of course, the title was meant to conjure up the idea that we were going to read something out of the ordinary.) The same, I would argue, goes for the cultural landscape of The Netherlands: we are a nation known for its painters (Rembrandt to Van Gogh), architects (Rem Koolhaas) and photographers (Ed van der Elsken) – their talents all easily recognisable since they do not need the language to communicate.

For somebody who is interested in international fiction or novels in translation, The Netherlands could seem like a flat land – because few writers have made it to that elusive thing: the international,

award-winning bestseller. But there are in fact Dutch mountains, metaphorically speaking, and this special guest feature of Banipal is showcasing some outstanding new contemporary names in Dutch literature. On behalf of the Dutch Foundation for Literature in Amsterdam, where it is my task to keep foreign publishers informed about new books from Holland, I am grateful to Margaret Obank for giving me the opportunity to do this.

The six writers here share nothing except for the fact they are all writing in the same language. Does that make them literary relatives? I am not sure. When you write your first novel, do you write about your childhood in an Amsterdam suburb or do you look elsewhere for inspiration? One of the youngest names here, the poet Jan-Willem Anker, made his debut as a novelist with a fictional account of the life of Lord Elgin, who famously stole the marble sculptures and reliefs from the Acropolis, the 'Elgin Marbles' on display in the British Museum. The first chapter, which is included here, focuses on the death of the father of Lord Elgin when he was still a boy. Heartbreaking and meticulously written – but nothing Dutch about its theme.

Stephan Enter enjoyed success with his breakthrough novel called *Grip* in 2012. It has been translated into several languages, but not yet English or Welsh, and was awarded two major literary prizes. The story is about a group of four friends who are on a reunion trip in Wales to celebrate their 20-year friendship: three men, one woman. It appears that all the men have been in love with her – and that the one who won her heart was not the one who loved her the most. Enter's way of writing resembles that other great Dutch writer, Willem Frederik Hermans: by telling a story in such a controlled way, the reader can't do anything but surrender to the ideas of the writer. It was Hermans who famously said we live in a 'sadistic universe', and Enter's story is an example of that.

Everything That Was Left by Hanna Bervoets is a non-chronological account from the eyes of TV editor Merel, who is trapped inside a building, where a TV show was being recorded, when an enormous explosion goes off outside. Nobody can leave, and nobody knows what has happened. As food supplies dwindle, tensions mount. How do we adapt to a radically new situation? What do we have to give up? And if everything that once was is no more, what do loyalty and friendship mean?

In *The Disappearance of Robbert*, Robbert Welagen plays a witty game, full of self-mockery, with his own life as a writer. The Robbert who disappears is also called Welagen. He is a twenty-five-year-old writer who, like the author, has written a novel entitled Lipari that won him a prize for the year's best first novel. The longing to just step off the face of the earth seems to be present in other books from Holland, too, but this is a short novel which in the end is a moving story about unrequited love.

An author who started publishing his work later in his career, Benjamin Burg is the author of two short story collections and one novel, written with the atmosphere, control and maturity of similar American authors, such as Raymond Carver, John Cheever or Kevin Canty. The art of leaving things out is his speciality, and he does it to great effect in his understated short stories, such as "Restaurant Des Arenes", in which a divorced father has dinner with his children. Finally, the author whose work reflects the traditional Dutch landscape the most is Franca Treur, who made a spectacular debut with *Confetti on the Threshing Floor*, a semi-autobiographical account about growing up in the Netherlands's Protestant Bible Belt – where pop music, drugs, prositution and euthanasia are all mentioned in the same shameful, sinful vein. After being cheeky to her mother, the main character dreams that when Judgment Day comes around, God banishes her to hell: 'The Lord God looks at her and says: Remove her from My sight. Cast her into outer darkness, where there will be weeping and wailing and gnashing of teeth.'

These are not necessarily Dutch writers, these are just six contemporary writers who in their work devote themselves to themes such as doomsday, divorce, disappearance, religion, friendship and theft of art. I recommend their work and hope that one day their books will be available in English.

FRANCA TREUR

A lodge in a garden
of cucumbers

AN EXCERPT FROM THE NOVEL
CONFETTI ON THE THRESHING FLOOR,
TRANSLATED BY LAURA WATKINSON

It all started with a stale biscuit. 'I'm not eating those dusty old things,' Katelijne said rebelliously. 'At Aunt Mattie's they have sticky buns with their coffee after the Sunday service.' Mother called her an ungrateful little brat: 'And anyway how do you know the biscuits are stale? Couldn't keep your paws off, eh?' This accusation is now hanging like a balloon over their heads, welcoming the large grey clouds that are floating towards them over the dunes, watched very closely by nine pairs of eyes, because the hay is out drying.

'You can't trust the weather forecast one inch,' Father says and that's all he'll say on the subject, because he must place his trust in the Lord. He's speaking to no one in particular, but the people occupying the white plastic chairs on the freshly mown and sprinkled lawn have all heard and each of them is trying to think of an appropriate response, but there isn't one. It wasn't the subject in church that morning; who preaches about crops and toil in this day and age?

The hay was already as good as dry on Saturday. But Father didn't want to start baling it yet. Pelleboer the weatherman had talked about yet more high pressure and didn't mention clouds, not even a wisp. 'I'll wait,' Father had said. 'A few hours of strong sunshine and Monday will be a fine day for making hay.' But the sunset last night hadn't looked good.

In the scrubby adjoining meadow, where the recent drought has left hardly anything juicy and tender behind, the cows reach longingly over the barbed wire, tempted by the scent of the freshly mown lawn. Grass is always greener on the other side.

'Dead to the law by the body of Christ,' Katelijne recites. 'One: the law curses the sinner. Two: the law condemns the sinner. And three . . .' She hesitates. 'I had it just a second ago,' she says anxiously. Curses, condemns, what was the third point again? She swings her feet backwards and forwards and the edge of the seat cuts into the flesh at the back of her knees.

'The law kills the sinner,' she says with a sigh of relief.

Father nods. 'Do you remember the reading too?'

Katelijne thinks for a moment. It was from Galatians, but there's no need for her to answer now, because a car comes past and everyone turns to look at the road, which very few people come down. The little ones stand on tiptoe to peer over the bushes.

'Koosje and her dog,' Father announces, stretching his neck like a heron. The dog is running down the grass verge alongside the car, with its tongue lolling out of its mouth. Someone declares that it's criminal of her to drive so quickly, which is completely unnecessary, because everyone agrees on that subject and she flies past too quickly every day. But still it feels good to voice such feelings and so there's always someone who says it's criminal and that Koosje needs to get up off her lazy behind.

Other such frequently repeated statements are: that you'd never ever want to live in the village, that you'd never in a million years want to live in town or work in an office, that milk from a carton is undrinkable and that the best time to spread muck is when the wind's blowing towards the village.

'I'd like to go for a drive in Koosje's car some time,' Rogier, the eldest brother, growls. 'And then she could run along beside it until her tongue was sticking out of her gob. And you can bet I wouldn't keep under the speed limit.' It's not the first time he's said that either.

'But it's ages until you're eighteen,' Katelijne says.

'I know how to drive a car, though,' he says. 'I drive the tractor, don't I?'

That's true. He's already driving it on the farm and around the yard. Not on the road yet though, because he needs a tractor driving licence first and you have to be sixteen for that. He can actually drive better than Father, because Father sometimes forgets to drop the front loader when he drives through the barn doors and they're only designed with the height of a snorting horse in mind.

Not that the barn is any the wiser, of course. It always remains in blissful ignorance. During the war, it even stood up to its knees in water for a while, but you wouldn't know that now. The only sign is a line running just above the rusty anchor plates; the salt has changed the colour of the joints from the ground up to that point, that's all.

'But yesterday you were driving around like a headless chicken,' says Christiaan, the second brother, who goes to special school and spends the rest of his time trying to catch Rogier out.

Christiaan produces rivalry just as he produces sweat, or his daily turd, which he then faithfully places at the feet of his first-born brother in the hope that he'll slip and fall flat on his face in it one day. He does this to assert his right to his own place in the pecking order (Father's pecking order, in which Rogier has for years been the undisputed leader). And that's also the reason why he's started bringing home nuts and bolts and nails that he 'found somewhere on the way to school'.

It began a few weeks ago. Rogier came home with a screw that he'd seen lying on the ground. It was still shiny; it had never been used.

'A self-tapper,' Father said, flicking it with his finger. 'Look, it's got a drill point on it too.' He put it in his trouser pocket, gave Rogier an appreciative nod and said, 'That's going to come in handy some time.'

The next day Christiaan suddenly placed two wing nuts on the tablecloth and three days later a bolt and a cap nut. All of them brand spanking new. They all agreed that he'd pilfered them from his school workshop and Father obviously told him he had to stop right away, but Christiaan said indignantly that he was just keeping his eyes open on the way to school these days.

'Yeah, I bet. All the way from here to the bus stop,' Rogier said, and then of course it all turned into another row, just the way things are heading now, following Christiaan's comment about the 'headless chicken'.

The little ones side with Rogier and their chubby hands start thumping away at Christiaan's knees, which have a beige pair of trousers stretched around them on Sundays, not denim (those are just for weekdays). Katelijne lines up squarely behind Christiaan, not because he's right, but because it's Christiaan, and he's always the underdog whenever Rogier's involved. Finally, there's Jeroen, the third brother, who tends to come out in favour of Rogier and whatever it is that Rogier's in favour of – with the exception of red-and-white cows, because Jeroen is the only one in the family who prefers black-and-white ones. Jeroen has ideas all of his own, which don't depend on anyone else at all. But what's more important than his ideas is his unparalleled skill at calming skittish animals. He's already managed to save Father a lot of trouble.

Mother asks if that's what they learned at church, that bickering, and says she'd like to enjoy a quiet cup of coffee just for once, and Father shouts, 'That's enough', and then another car comes past, driving slowly. A Passat, according to Rogier, who is always quick to notice things like that. The car has a German number plate.

'Bloody Kraut,' Christiaan says.

'With a Hitler moustache,' says Rogier, making stuff up.

'They all have Hitler moustaches,' says Christiaan, who always swallows that sort of nonsense. You can make Christiaan believe anything. When they're lying in bed at night and Jeroen 'reminds' him that he hasn't said his prayers, he kneels right down beside his bed and starts singing 'Now I lay me down to sleep', even though he did it only five minutes before.

'He should go back to Krautland,' says Lourens, which sounds particularly amusing coming from the mouth of someone who isn't even four yet.

'Who teaches you to say that kind of thing?' Mother says, but she's laughing too and so the whole family's happy again.

The sun looks increasingly like an egg yolk from a chicken that hasn't eaten any greens – and that's not a good sign. You shouldn't be able to look at the sun; if you can, it's not strong enough to dry the grass. In the Bible, the prayer of one believer, the prophet Elijah, is enough to make it rain after a time of serious drought. Unfortunately it doesn't appear to work the other way around, when you want to stop the rain. Nine children of the Lord on a medium-sized lawn who would like to turn the hands of the clock forward until work once again becomes a sacred duty and not a forbidden act are apparently not enough to change a thing about the weather, so they will have to stand by and watch in resignation as the rain turns the potentially perfect hay into pale, musty rubbish that no cow would want to eat and which will lie overheating in the hayloft until it becomes a danger to them all.

Just after midday, at a quarter past twelve, Father sends everyone to bed, so that he can go himself, along with Mother. Most of them actually try to sleep, instead of reading a book in bed as they do in the winter. If they're snoring contentedly, they hope that Father won't wake them at two o'clock and they can at least escape the afternoon service. It's hardly worth even trying, because Father has no problem pulling the covers off them, but the trick worked once and if it worked once, it might work again. Katelijne, who can't sleep in the middle of the day anyway, intends to put down her book at ten to two and then pretend.

She's leaning on her elbow, reading a book she got from school as a Christmas present. She's already read it three times, but she's read all of the books in the library, so she doesn't have much choice. She's not really concentrating on the book though, because she has a hole in her stomach and it's rather noisy. In fact, it's really very noisy indeed for a hole that's the size of a stale biscuit.

She knows Mother doesn't have anything nice in the cupboards. 'Sweets are junk,' is Mother's simple motto. Against her own better judgement, Katelijne sneaks down to the kitchen anyway (Father and Mother's bedroom is directly above it). Her bare feet slap quietly against the floor tiles and she almost stumbles over the buckets by the washing machine. Mother uses them to catch the rinse water, which she says is still clean enough for scrubbing the floor or flushing out the loo. In the kitchen the cupboard doors creak accusingly and the barrels and biscuit tins that she ferrets out make their own hollow metal sounds. Empty, all empty too.

A sandwich then. Carefully she navigates the butter dish over the jar of peanut butter. The lid of the butter dish can fly off really easily and it makes a terrible racket when you tap Morse code on it with your knife, let alone when it crashes onto the hard floor. The brown Brabantia breadbin makes such a loud grating noise too; it's as old as Vlissingen. Now just the chocolate spread, which of course has to be right at the back. Ten minutes of acrobatics later, everything's on the kitchen table and all she needs is a knife.

Just as she's got the kitchen drawer open, she hears a car slowing down and turning up their drive. Visitors on the day of rest are as rare here as sweets in the jar, and they've picked a pretty inconvenient time to turn up too. Katelijne watches as the innocent pot of chocolate spread transforms into a vessel of temptation. The butter dish leaves behind a slick and sleazy smear of grease and the bread looks ashamed at enticing her to the filthy sin of eating.

Is there any way to avoid a slap on the behind now?

Katelijne hurries out on her bare feet through the patio doors to the drive, where a woman has got out of the passenger side of the car. She has short hair, painted lips and earrings and she's wearing trousers. A man is sitting at the wheel and in the back seat is a boy of about ten with a face as pale as a sugar beet and brown eyes that are far too big. It's the Passat that drove past before.

'*Ist deine Mutti irgendwo?*'

'What?' Katelijne says.

'*Dein Vati oder deine Mutti? Sind sie da?*' As though the woman knows that her mother and father must be there somewhere, she projects the shrill words past the honeysuckle and the Virginia creeper up to the window with its crocheted curtains and the dried bridal bouquet.

'No,' Katelijne says quietly. She looks up. No sign of movement behind the curtains as yet; her parents are not likely to sacrifice their Sunday afternoon nap to engage in corrective punishment, but there are no guarantees, just as eighty years of faithful churchgoing offer no surety for the fate of the soul in the hereafter.

The woman looks from Katelijne to the car to the sky, with disappointment on her face. The sky appears to be eliciting sympathy for their plight by turning the colour of the sand used to fill horse paddocks. Before long, puddles will render much of the land hereabouts inaccessible for both man and beast.

'*Vor es zu regnen anfängt, wollen wir das Zelt aufgeschlagen haben.*' She brings her fingertips together to make the pointed roof of a tent. 'But everywhere is full. Could we please stay here for just one night? *Wir würden dir sehr erkenntlich sein.*' She points at the grass beside the drive, where they have their swing and the rabbit run with two black-and-white Giant Papillons in it.

Do they want to camp here beside the house? Father and Mother will never allow that. No strangers running around in their garden.

Katelijne shakes her head. It's not going to work.

'*Er ist krank,*' the woman says. She points at the boy in the back of the car. He stares at Katelijne with his cow eyes. She isn't used to that much direct attention and suddenly realises she's standing there in her nightie.

'Er ist *krank*,' the woman repeats.

Krank. Katelijne runs the word through her mind. It means 'sick'. The Lord Jesus once used that word Himself. 'I was sick, and ye visited me,' He said. 'Inasmuch as ye have done it to one of the least of these my brethren, ye have done it unto me.'

In some Bibles, every word that the Lord Jesus actually said Himself is printed in red. Her teacher at school told them about it.

Katelijne points at the grass. 'Okay, there then,' she says, giving in, because that's how it feels: as though something stronger than her is forcing her to speak.

'*Ach, vielen Dank. Wann kommen deine Eltern wieder?*'

Katelijne can feel the woman looking her up and down, from head to toe. She wants to tell her that she's wearing her nightdress because . . . actually, why is she? Who goes to bed in the middle of the day?

'I *krank* too,' she says, pointing at the pink bear on her tummy. The words are out before she realises and suddenly her parents are no longer lying behind those yellowing curtains, but are racing like mad to find a doctor to cure her illness. She likes that image: Mother saying 'Oh, Arjaon. Don't drive so quickly,' and Father answering furiously that he is prepared to go to any extreme to help his daughter.

'*Ach so,*' the woman says, and her chilly gaze suddenly becomes a look of sympathy, which Katelijne prefers, if she's honest. '*Wann kommen deine Eltern wieder?*'

Katelijne doesn't understand. 'There,' she says, pointing again. 'There, by the swing.'

The woman gets back into the car with her husband and son and they drive up close to the grass. Back in the kitchen, Katelijne returns to making her sandwich because it's time to think of herself now after all that charity. Then she hides it under her nightie, but it won't stay there – it does stay put when she tucks it inside the elastic of her pants though – and she makes herself another one. Lids and cupboards shut, crumbs brushed off the table, no one any the wiser.

Munching away behind the nets of her small bedroom window, she watches the man as he spreads the tent out on the ground. The woman says something and takes hold of one of the ends of the tent. The man shrugs his shoulders, the woman shakes her head and points up at the sky, which is about to burst open like a juicy sun-ripened tomato. They turn the tent ninety degrees.

The boy is kneeling on the back seat, with his elbows on the parcel shelf and something in his hands that looks like a Rubik's cube. Again he looks straight into Katelijne's eyes, and she shrinks away, but not for long. Only God and her conscience can see her standing there behind the curtains.

Katelijne suspects that Father and Mother will be angry, because they're not keen on strangers, but she had no choice. The men on the road to Emmaus did not recognise the Lord Jesus when He walked with them and when they invited Him into their house. God forbid that you might send Him away.

The tent's up. The man is tying ropes to the poles of the swing and fixing them in the ground with pegs. It's a high, almost square tent, the colour of milky coffee, with dark-brown zips.

The boy is allowed out of the car now. He's wearing jeans and a black jumper with yellow stripes and carrying his pillow under his free arm. He looks at the house one more time, where Katelijne is spying through a window in a small room, and then he disappears into the tent with his father. The mother follows with a blanket.

Katelijne has had enough of standing there, because the lino's cold on her feet, but she feels responsible, like a lifeguard at the open-air swimming pool. She needs something high to sit on. There's a cupboard unit from Grandmother's old kitchen up against the window, which is now used for Katelijne's clothes. She can't sit on that though; it doesn't have a top, just a pale-blue bath towel, and when she pulls that away, she's looking straight into the cutlery drawer full of knickers, cotton tights and rolled-up socks.

She lifts her desk chair (which also began its career in Grandmother's kitchen) onto the bed, but that's much too wobbly and also too far from the window. So she puts it against the windowsill and piles it high with books from her only bookshelf. Sitting on top of that, she has a perfect view of the German man coming out of the milking shed with a bottle in his hands, presumably full of water that he's taken from the low tap. His wife stoops as she comes out of the tent and says something to him, pointing at their house. The man shakes his head. The bottle, which he was holding aloft like plundered booty, sinks down; it would seem there are suddenly more important issues. The boy comes out of the tent and joins in the conversation. His parents look at him seriously, listen to what he says and then nod. He takes a few steps forwards, leaving his parents standing a couple of metres behind him, and fiddles with his trousers. His mother rushes forward to help, but he pushes her away and manages it all by himself. He pees in an arc against the rabbit run, as though his parents aren't standing there watching him with worried faces.

But it's good to be hospitable, Katelijne thinks. Even when your guests have just peed all over your rabbit run and are now eating a banana on your swing.

'What's all this then?' Father's standing in the doorway with his bandy white legs, dark-blue socks on his feet and a saggy pair of pants above. He is looking in surprise at Katelijne, who is still sitting on top of her books by the window. Then he sees the German car through the nets, and the tent, which the family have just crawled inside, because it's started raining so hard that everything is soaked through, like cardboard that's fallen into a puddle. That certainly includes the tent and the hay.

'They're sheltering here from the rain. There was no room for them anywhere else and they have a sick little boy with them.' Luckily it comes out just as she's rehearsed.

'Is this all your doing? Why didn't you call us?'

Katelijne gets it in the neck, especially from Mother, who comes to join Father, with her liver-coloured tights already on beneath her nightdress. She would never do something like that without first consulting Father. Her fury is fierce and comes quickly, as though it's been lying in wait for some time.

'I can't go to church like this,' Father says. And then the anger begins all over again. Hadn't Katelijne thought about this? You're completely tied down when you have strangers on your property.

'You think you can just do whatever you like.'

'They'll need to use the toilet too,' Mother suddenly gasps, already picturing brown German stripes in the loo.

'Yes, and tonight as well,' Father says. 'So the door will have to stay open all night. If we let them stay here, that is.'

Mother's against the idea, but Father thinks it's not right to just send them away. The decision is made that Mother will go to church now, with Katelijne and the boys, and that Father should stay here with little Lourens. Then they'll talk about it again this evening.

Excerpted from *Dorsvloer vol confetti* (Confetti on the Threshing Floor) by Franca Treur, published by Prometheus, Amsterdam, 2009.

AUTHOR

Photo: © Mark Van der Zouw

ROBBERT WELAGEN

The Disappearance
of Robbert

AN EXCERPT FROM THE NOVEL,
TRANSLATED FROM THE DUTCH BY DAVID DOHERTY

It is better to act and repent,
than not to act and regret.
– Machiavelli

1

I had come up with a plan – to leave on the spur of the moment. My apartment was almost empty. Only the essentials remained: a bed and a lamp. I had sold or thrown away most of what I owned. Everything I had left could fit in a suitcase. It was a big suitcase, mind you.

I had one reason for throwing my things away: to disappear without trace one day. It had begun as a flight of fancy and now it had taken over my life.

Four days it had taken me to get rid of my possessions. Pretty good going when you think how many years it took to accumulate them all.

An antique dealer bought the Czech table my father and mother had given me on my eighteenth birthday. The tabletop had a decorative red and yellow border painted with flowers. I had been to the Czech Republic and the first provincial railway station I laid eyes on was decorated with the same motif.

The table was a charming companion to the pale green marble-topped sideboard, purchased from a little shop while I was living in my first student digs.

The top drawer of the sideboard was where I kept souvenirs. Among them was a coin-shaped token, dark blue with the words 'Literary Gala' printed on it. No year; perhaps the tokens were meant to be reused. I had written a book called Lipari and after it was published, I took Chloe to the Literary Gala. Chloe and I had studied together, shared a house and been on holiday together. Along the way I had fallen in love with her but she saw me as a good friend, nothing more. It's not easy when one of your few friends is a young woman whose intellect you respect and who is physically attractive into the bargain. Especially not when she wants to join you on a one-tent camping trip, invites you to feel how smooth her freshly shaved legs are and reads books like Milan Kundera's *Slowness*. We went for dozens of walks. She ate my bread and honey. No one could arch her eyebrow so fetchingly while recounting how her day had been. The time when she developed a keen interest in sex and eroticism (she was reading the essays of Georges Bataille) didn't make things any easier: with me, she only talked sex. I nurtured the silent hope that one day she would see me as a lover. By taking her to the Literary Gala I believed I was accelerating that process. The bounty I had envisioned didn't exactly materialise. She danced with other men, on the stage, as if it were all a play. I sat on one of the seats in the darkness of the stalls. She thought it was a fun night out. Chloe had the enviable quality of being content with the mediocre life people are obliged to lead once their youth is over.

Next to the token was a swimming cap I had worn one afternoon at a public pool near Turin, fourteen summers before my departure. My parents and my brother lay by the pool sunbathing while I leapt from the diving board.

Then there was a button from my favourite coat, the penknife I was given on my seventh birthday, a shell found during a walk on the beach, a die, a wristband and some keys. Postage stamps, my broken fountain pen and old tennis club membership cards.

The second drawer held letters from girlfriends I'd had between the ages of sixteen and twenty: funny, sweet, passionate, heartbroken letters. No new ones arrived and I took to rereading them. Who are loving words meant for when the girl who wrote them is no longer in love with the boy they were written to?

The bottom drawer contained bank statements, diaries, envelopes, pencils and yet-to-be-used picture frames.

I tipped the contents of the three drawers into a bin bag. As for the sideboard, I sold it off to the antique dealer who bought the table. With it went the brass lamp, the bowl and my grandfather's pocket watch.

A bookseller bought up nearly all my books – I set a small pile aside to take with me. He came to my door, surveyed the contents of my bookcases and concluded that they contained little of value, by which he meant no rare copies or first editions. There were mainly humble second-hand volumes of prose, a few poetry anthologies and a shelf of books about art. I received a decent price all the same. He took them away on the spot, in those special flat-pack book boxes. I helped with the carrying.

The empty bookcases, the couch and what was left of the stereo equipment (record player and cassette deck having fallen by the wayside years ago) were picked up by two men from a charity shop. They also took my mobile phone and my computer, as well as kitchen utensils, a vase, the acoustic guitar and the waste paper basket.

I tossed photograph albums and stray photos into a second bin bag and deposited both bags on the curb for collection.

I took almost all of my clothes and shoes to a clothing bank. Those I kept were selected for their inconspicuousness. I had a preference for grey and brown, but not everything brown would do. For instance, a few months before I came up with the plan to disappear from my life, I bought a brand new pair of shoes, a brown pair made by Crockett & Jones of England. I might add that this was during my 'natty period'. In those shoes, I looked like I had just strolled out of some Oxford drama society en route to my Granny's weekly crochet circle. Elderly ladies eyed me approvingly.

For a while, I took a certain pleasure in wearing the shoes. But once the plan was in place, they no longer passed muster. The thing was, they made a noise. When the heels hit the pavement, they announced that I was coming. And – more to the point – that I was going.

So shoes and heels wound up at the clothing bank too and I reverted to the well-trodden, soundless pair I had worn before.

Without the above items, these obtrusive reminders of myself, I already felt a good deal more transparent.

My preparations continued. I fastened a belt around the suitcase, just to be sure. You never can tell. I could picture the awkwardness and embarrassment of my suitcase falling open as I walked down the street, my underpants spilling out for all to see. I was about to leave my life but I had yet to shake off the prude in me.

I positioned the suitcase by the front door, as close to my departure as possible. All I had to do was take a run-up.

There were three locks on the door: one at the top, one in the middle and one at the bottom. These I removed for fear of losing my keys... Then what would I do?

Open my front door and the first thing you see is the lift. Not that I was planning to use something so unreliable. The stairs, that was more like it! I had started taking the stairs frequently to get a feel for them. It was easy to slip in smooth soles, so I either had to avoid wearing smooth soles or tread very calmly. I opted for the former.

I also opened the window and left it open. When you leave on the spur of the moment, who says you have to use the door?

It was a first floor window that looked out onto a shopping street where people walked down the pavement and cars drove past. I slotted a stick between frame and sill, as it had a tendency to slide shut suddenly and unexpectedly. Wouldn't it be typical: the window is open for days and just as you're clambering out, suitcase in hand, it comes slamming down on your head.

When setting out on a journey, you need to be in good shape. I was tall and skinny. Press-ups seemed like a good idea. I started with two, then panted for a good thirty seconds, wiping imaginary sweat from my brow. Admittedly, that last bit was purely for show. From then on I did press-ups every morning, without adding so much as a millimetre to my biceps.

Broadly speaking, these were the preparations I made.

In my empty apartment, I tried to work out why it was that I wanted to leave. I traced every train of thought. An answer was not forthcoming. All I found were reasons that failed to convince. I didn't believe them in any case; perhaps you will take a kinder view.

One was that I'd had enough of myself and my life. It was all too familiar to me, I had spent too much time there and I wanted to cancel my membership. I felt an unremitting sadness, I never slept, I was twenty-five and – apart from writing Lipari – I saw my life as a failure.

Something remained permanently unfulfilled and gnawed away at me constantly. Something had been making my head ache for years. I didn't know what it was. Just life itself, I suppose.

True, when I was writing, I did feel I was worth at least something. I fell into a blissful state and forgot that I existed. But in the leftover hours of the day, there was still a life to be led. I was not fond of the everyday. A dreary round of motions to be gone through; that was all it ever amounted to.

It seems every human being has to accept a measure of sorrow in his life. The question is, how much?

I was unable to enter into the happiness of family and friends and so they would leave me behind one day, as inevitably as a weak animal is cast out of the pack. It was a rejection I would be unable to face. It was better to beat them to it and leave.

There was another thing that didn't help much: Chloe married someone else.

I said to her: 'This isn't what we agreed.'

She said: 'We didn't agree anything.'

I attended the wedding at the town hall. My look of dismay was taken for a fonder emotion. I congratulated Chloe's father and mother. I congratulated her husband's father and mother. I gave the bride and groom a gift. I watched as they were photographed. They looked happy.

I tried to write a story about that day. As a writer, what else is there to do? Nothing came of it and other attempts, on other subjects, also led nowhere. The sentences I wrote felt bogus and contrived. Rather than making a character in a story disappear, I wanted to disappear myself.

My contact with Chloe dwindled. When she called me, I seldom called back. She was none too pleased by this, but what would have been the point? Words... I wanted more than words.

Meanwhile I won a best debut prize for *Lipari*. My publisher had faith in me and the critics dubbed me 'a bright new talent'. Despite all this, I'd already given up writing.

In the weeks before my debut and the wedding, I had felt for the first time in my life that things were looking up. My book was as good as finished and there was this girl I liked. When that book of mine is published, I thought, happiness will be closer. I was twenty-four and buoyed by the notion that my life was about to take shape.

But once my book was in the shops, nothing changed. I had simply got something stuck in my head. It had all been just a daydream in the shade. One strip of sunlight from the real world and it was gone.

It was best to start believing in something else, something other than literature and love. In an idea that would keep me fully occupied. You need something to keep you occupied in life: a lifelong disappearance without trace, unattached and unassailable.

Are you convinced by these melodramatic reasons? I can't say I am, not fully in any case. Who's to say I wouldn't have come up with this plan if I'd led another life? I mean, perhaps it's genetic.

It's not like you can ask Michelangelo Antonioni why Anna vanished from his film L'Avventura. All we know is that after her friends' futile search, life went on. People can't stop falling in love, eating, talking and driving around in cars. So long as you're alive, that's more or less all you can do. But God knows, I'd had my fill.

It's a relief when someone is forgotten; that's what Antonioni seems to be saying. Besides, it's biology pure and simple. The ones left behind are fixed on the future and put their own survival first.

I wanted to become a memory. One day we'll all become a memory, but I couldn't wait.

At twenty-five, your youth is pretty much behind you. I was my own responsibility. My parents had given me a life to do with as I pleased. Some see it as a gift. I did too, but as a gift I left unopened.

Speaking for myself, my departure would not be the first day of the rest of my life. At least, that seemed like too sweeping a statement. The person Robbert Welagen would cease to exist, but without thinking of weighty conceits like 'the end' and 'epilogue'. Whatever happened, I would no longer be around for other people. But I would, I feared, still be around for myself.

I had thrown away my things because I couldn't bear for my parents to have to do it once I was gone. In that sense, an empty apartment was the lesser of two evils.

In the event that a gravestone had to be picked out for me, I had an inscription in mind. A line from a children's book, said with a smile: 'To die will be an awfully big adventure.'

I didn't yet know when I would leave. It might be the next day. Or in two weeks' time. The main thing was that I had a plan. And when you have a plan, all you have to do is act on it.

Excerpted from *The Disappearance of Robbert*,
published by Nijgh & Van Ditmar, Amsterdam 2013

Photo: © Roeland Fossen

STEPHAN ENTER

GRIP

AN EXCERPT FROM THE NOVEL,
TRANSLATED FROM THE DUTCH BY MICHELE HUTCHISON

1

Christ, there he was. Paul van Woerden was standing at the till with his wallet open, happened to look past the sales assistant and spotted him going past. Yes, it was him, no doubt about it: Vincent Voogd, that most agile of alpinists, instantly recognisable after twenty years. That same surly face with its patchy sideburns. He was wearing a fashionable herringbone jacket, pulled a small wheely case behind him like a recalcitrant dog and held up a newspaper at eye level. He was so engrossed that he bumped into someone while reading and – this was just typical – instead of offering his apologies appeared to receive them.

The saleswoman wrapped Paul's purchase in silver paper and tied a shiny ribbon around it. Paul thanked her with a smile but was rebuffed by the cherry red score of her mouth. He picked up his rucksack, hoisted it onto his shoulder and made his way to the main concourse.

He couldn't see Vincent at first; in just a few minutes Bruxelles Midi had become twice as busy. There was movement everywhere, a dozen different languages droned through the space, and a pack of school children lay siege to a stall selling intoxicatingly scented waffles. Further along, in the lower hall he'd be making his way to shortly, there was a queue at the check-in desk – but Vincent wasn't there yet. Paul walked to an open space in front of a kiosk and set his bag down before him. The buttercup yellow Eurostar logo shone at him discreetly, along the length of the underground station gleamed confectioners, an off-licence, a coffee bar, a perfumery and all sorts of shops and he had a brief vision of an enchanted grotto in which all faces were full of expectation – each traveller abandoning their worldly possessions and preparing for a journey to the centre of the earth.

Pickpockets active, resounded through the hall. Take care of your luggage, s'il vous plaît. Paul drummed the gift with his fingertips. He filled his lungs (how delicious those waffles smelled!), straightened up in an attempt to see over the top of everyone and everything and suddenly became aware of a stirring enthusiasm, a feeling of happiness rising within him. He chuckled to himself – how little one changes in the end! A glimpse, a barb of memory and he was immediately won over again by Vincent. But back then Vincent had won everyone over – with his daring, and the curious ease with which he put things into perspective, including himself – for Vincent knew very well that he was a shameless go-getter, eager to show who could climb the best, who could read a map with the greatest accuracy and who could erect a tent the fastest. That one time – by the side of a glassy reservoir in Wallis where they waited around for half an hour because Martin had skimmed a pebble which bounced nine times and Vincent wouldn't go on until he'd managed ten and didn't realise that the entire gang were making fun of him. Afterwards you wondered why no one got annoyed – but you had to know what Vincent was like, you had to experience his disarming cheerfulness.

Paul began to feel warm, took off his anorak and laid it over his bag. And, he thought with a mixture of self-mockery and embarrassment, while he pictured himself at that lake (nineteen or twenty, thin as a rake, nose and neck burned red and hair bleached by the sun) – how intensely he'd longed to be like that too, to change and take on Vincent's cast iron mentality, capable of peeling off doubt and replacing it with a layer of shimmering courage. Christ, you couldn't help but feel like an idiot if you remembered what you were like as a student! Even if you could see now that it was a part of that biting itself in the tail age group – so frantic you were to conceal and correct every shortcoming in your personality! But this, he thought as he looked around and listened to the cacophony of languages and smelled the sweet aroma of waffles, this does change as you get older: you don't take everything to heart, what others think of you causes a light graze at worst. And looking back, wasn't it a wonder that you hadn't made a bigger mess of things considering your own hopelessness? But look, there was Vincent again – ambling along, tapping his newspaper softly against his leg and craning his neck, his lower lip jutting out critically, to study the irrelevant departure times of the local trains on the signs hanging from the ceiling in the hall.

Paul collected his belongings and walked up to him. 'What ho!' he said – which was strange because he never greeted anyone like that. It also came out of his mouth much more loudly than he'd intended. And from nowhere the memory of how their very first meeting began with Vincent's question as to whether that 'fissure' in his chin was hereditary.

STEPHAN ENTER

He clamped the package under his arm and stuck out his hand. Vincent gave him a surprised look and shook his hand weakly. Now that he stood before him (they were exactly the same height), Paul saw just how little Vincent had changed. Yes, practically identical, he thought. And now everything came back! That first impression of stiffness and reticence and then the involuntary feeling of being privileged (it was almost gratitude) when Vincent automatically included you in something. A few wrinkles fanned out around Vincent's eyes, his facial features might have sharpened but his skin had a healthy colour, his cheeks even had a bloom. Not even the slightest trace of his going bald or grey. Yes, miraculous – the way he stood here again, straight as a rod, the unadulterated willpower he exuded.

'You did know I was coming?' Paul asked brightly.

'I didn't know anything,' Vincent said. 'Well… did think you might be flying.' He peered at Paul's gift.

'Coffee!' Paul said. 'Exclusive coffee, if I'm to believe them. Couldn't think of anything else but it seems appropriate if Martin makes good on his promise.'

Vincent nodded with the stirrings of a smile. Naturally he hadn't forgotten how Martin was the first to unzip his tent each morning, how he woke the others with professional élan, planned the day and made a pot of coffee so poisonously strong your stomach wrenched.

'Have you got anything?' Paul asked.

Vincent nodded. A bottle of Japanese whisky, in Japanese wrapping. 'And,' he added, 'that's no laughing matter. Turns out it's a whole art form – even if the Japanese do pronounce everything art sooner or later, including themselves.' He still had that line around his peculiarly wide mouth that suggested unpredictability and adventure. At the same time there was something tired in his gaze; of course he'd got up early to catch the train to Brussels. Paul realised that although Vincent had been working for around five years at a meteorological institute in Tokyo, it still wasn't exactly clear to him what he did. They'd lost touch for a while and it was only in recent months that they'd begun to exchange emails regularly again. In his last missive, Vincent had casually announced that he'd be going to Martin's too – he'd be visiting his parents in Zeeland and so was 'already in the neighbourhood'. He'd also said which train he'd be taking. Wasn't that a clear suggestion to travel together? It had helped Paul make up his mind – he had hesitated; up until then he'd been curious about how the others were doing, but Martin's invitation had been a surprise to him too.

'Well!' Paul said again, hearing himself. But it was too late. Now he was gesturing towards the check-in desk and customs and announcing solemnly: 'If Mister Voogd would care to…'

They joined the other people waiting. The visit to his parents, Vincent told Paul when he enquired, had lasted a couple of days too long. He had mainly spoken to his mother since his father was becoming too deaf and she'd kept on asking him when he'd marry a Japanese girl. She'd read that nine out of ten Europeans there intermarried and considered his remaining single the worst possible thing that could happen to anyone. Paul smiled but it was difficult to listen; Vincent suddenly seemed too alive to exist simultaneously in the deep branches of his memory. It was that voice, the way he spoke: with friendly disdain, undermining, as though everything he said about another he could say about you – it sounded improbably familiar. Back then when anyone had adopted that tone you knew they were imitating Vincent and for an instant, with a feeling that he had been jolted awake, he saw Vincent actually before him – in the middle of his student bedroom, a bright green book in his outstretched hand entitled *How to Improve your Relationship with Children*, and that voice, dry, 'Believe me, this is exactly how it works with girls.' And now it panned out to the way Vincent moved: somewhat stiffly and taking up too much room as though he didn't know what to do with his limbs – which greatly increased the impression he made as a mountaineer since he climbed like a gecko. Vincent had been offered a colleague's apartment (he spoke over his shoulder as he stood with his arms outstretched being searched by a customs officer), it was more rustic, though still in the city. But, he said, you couldn't really imagine Tokyo if you'd never been there. Contact with his colleagues remained strange, he had never managed to break through the ridiculous hierarchies and if he was honest, he had to admit that all of his acquaintances there were expats. Paul removed his watch from the conveyor belt and shook his wrist after putting it back on.

'Jesus,' Vincent said, 'is that still that watch with the cracked face?'

Paul nodded, with a degree of pride. That kind of comment nestled comfortably and familiarly in his ear and now – he hadn't thought about this for fifteen years – he remembered Vincent's habit of snatching flies out the air with one hand and slamming them down on a tabletop or flat stone so hard it would kill them.

They walked along the train. Paul counted the carriages, heard footsteps on the paving, as regular as the ticking of a clock. We're going away, we're going away. He looked – all those people studying their tickets wide-eyed, or cheerfully reaching down and lifting up luggage, or inhaling deeply on a final cigarette. How enraptured and electrified everything was! Everything soughed, everything breathed energy – and this was the essence of all large stations around Europe; this was how they glowed in his vision of them as stone beehives, how they lay in a web of iron blood vessels across continents, this was the source of a heartbeat that pumped life around the world. It occurred to him that it wasn't necessary to stick to the reserved seats. 'Martin emailed me that,' he said. 'A ruse the company uses – all the passengers in the first four coaches to make things easier for the staff.'

Vincent didn't seem to hear him, he had reached a hand into his trouser pocket and brought it out again, opened it. In his palm lay a teardrop shaped, pale grey pebble. Vincent rotated the stone a couple of times between his fingers without really looking at it and put it away again. And at the same moment, a knot of joy bursting in his chest, Paul was overcome with memories of other times, all the other times they'd pushed their way like this through the coaches of a waiting train on a sundrenched morning at the start of a couple of wonderful weeks.

So this was what it was like to see each other again! Freakish, as fragmented as looking in a cracked mirror – with needle sharp splinters and blind spots. And had Vincent always diffused this but did it used to be mixed up with his intransigency? Now it held Paul back – from asking questions and from basking in a pleasant conspiratorial irony. But Vincent didn't ask anything either. What if they had run out of things to say to each other and had to resort to old anecdotes to keep the conversation going? Well, so be it then. Yes, so be it, because this day was going to go well whatever it took.

'What were you reading by the way?' he asked.

'Sorry?'

'I saw you passing by back there – what was so thrilling in that newspaper that you went crashing into someone?'

Vincent stopped abruptly. He looked at Paul, his mouth slightly open. 'The dirty rascals,' he exclaimed. 'Keep an eye on this, will you?' And he'd already put his case down and was striding back towards customs.

'Leave it,' Paul shouted after him. 'We've only got a couple of minutes and it's not like you can just jump on the next train!'

But his tone was amused and contained little conviction. This was no surprise, it was Vincent down to a tee. This was Vincent's core, this was his concept of life – because he always believed that you could avert things: a four minute changeover upon which an international journey depended, or a ridge that must bear your entire weight, with kit, on tiptoes. Paul realised that he hadn't had enough sleep; a yawn swelled like a balloon against the roof of his mouth, he smothered it with his fist. He felt light-headed. He rubbed his clean shaven cheek and thought of summer and mountains. What a gift, what a mystery that you had everything at hand's reach all that time – but rarely looked at it, sometimes fleetingly like looking at a photo you'd once taken of a panorama; and that your memories ended up buried under rustling layers of new events, brimming with people and holidays and books and New Year's Eves and world revolutions and that now, simply because of accepting Martin's invitation and getting into a train, a breeze had stirred which had blown away all the piled up time and shown you that what lay underneath was as fresh and alive as twenty years ago.

And, cutting through a booming announcement in a ridiculous kind of Dutch, the sudden tension he'd felt whilst standing under the shower that morning returned – because he had a plan for today. Another seven or eight rushing hours and he'd see Lotte again for the first time in fourteen years. Was it really fourteen years ago? The wedding in that complicated castle-like house of her parents', all of the climbers present. On the phone she'd been cool and stern, and just like she used to she had scoffed at his high spirits – he remembered how she'd do something with her face, something that set her apart. She'd scowl – was that it? No, he'd seen her like that often enough, in front of a mountain cabin nursing a mug of tea in both hands, blowing it until it cooled. (She had noticeably long but not particularly elegant hands.) He could picture her face quite readily, her straight, dark blonde hair, her open-mouthed smile which half-bared her straight teeth – but she did something else, perhaps he was the only one to have noticed it. Or not, there was Martin too, of course. In any case, at one point, looking from a distance, it had occurred to him that you'd have to fall for that trait, or you'd hate her on the spot. Her chin – that's what it was. She'd jut her chin out imperiously to the side, away from you, after which she'd begin to chew on the inside of her cheek. He conjured her in his mind's eye – and now that noticeable, rather unattractive wrinkle appeared above her nose. But this didn't completely capture her, there was always something about Lotte that fluttered away from your mostly finely tuned senses – something behind a broken off sentence, an obstinate lock which she blew away from her face.

Here came Vincent again, the re-conquered newspaper rolled up into a cudgel.

2

A jolt, and brightly coloured billboards and dusty platform lights glided out of sight. And there was the blinding sun, slipping behind apartment blocks and offices and just as often leaping out again and turning away at the bends and casting glowing ribbons through the carriage – as though it were aware of mankind and seeking attention. And Paul squinted his eyes and followed, joining in. He had a seat next to the window, for the coming few hundred kilometres the sun would be travelling at his side. Yes, that's the way it goes, he thought; change the points, the earlier mood takes over and everything you imagined right up to a second before the encounter, gets swamped by something else.

It was as Martin had predicted: all the passengers bunched up together. And because when Vincent walked straight to his seat, he hadn't been sure whether to repeat that the reserved places were not sacrosanct, and now they were sitting diagonally opposite each other with strangers in between them. On Paul's right a woman in a floral dress studied the safety leaflet that had been lying on the collapsible table in front of them; opposite him sat an elderly couple: a heavy, audibly breathing man with large mottled hands fished a pair of horn-rimmed glasses from a case and his equally bespectacled wife quickly raised up Le Monde like a screen, as though she could feel Paul's gaze. He looked at Vincent on the other side of the aisle.

The older you became, he pondered, the less you understood other people's motivations. But actually it felt rather pleasant not to have to get into any deep conversations right away, and the fact that Vincent seemed self-absorbed – yes, this was convenient in some ways because all at once he wanted things to be like they used to be, for nothing to change for a moment. Perhaps this would help him gather his thoughts, he didn't have a clear idea of how he was going to tackle things later. He saw how the pure morning light illuminated Vincent's face right down to the pores. Vincent might be tired but the whites of his eyes were as clear as ice, the blue of his irises glowed with self-assurance and his mouth had a determined set. And how funny it was, his neat bearing, all considered. Exactly as one would imagine an European in Asia – still assuming colonial airs. Just now, when Vincent had stepped up onto the running-board and nimbly swung up his case, Paul had noticed that he was wearing thin socks under his shiny black brogues and he'd smelled a subtle and undoubtedly expensive fragrance. Were there no cracks? On Vincent's hand which was now mechanically rising to his forehead, the veins were almost slack – but he remembered a complaint Lotte's mother had made: that all mountaineers ended up with 'ugly monkey hands'. Maybe Vincent hadn't been up a mountain in ten years – or perhaps the opposite was true and he was still an active climber. The subject hadn't come up in any of their email exchanges.

He did things – that was Paul's impression of Vincent after that evening at the party of a practical stranger. When was that again? In his second year? And sometime in the first few weeks, because what had stuck in his mind was standing in front of a stickered door and reading the words Halls of Residence carved in runes – the summer had shaken off its greatest heat but evenings in the city were still honey coloured and filled with hopes that ran sky-high. And entering through a bare stairwell covered in empty bottles and phone directories, he saw Vincent with his whale-hunter's face, apparently the driving force behind a group who were preparing to depart. He recognised a few faces – climbers. Vincent glared condescendingly at someone who was saying that 'it was no great feat' if he didn't down a few more beers first, emptied his glass and left. Somebody nudged Paul, 'Come on, you have to see this.' He went along to have a look, the gang walked a few streets further, turned into a narrow high-walled alley and stopped halfway down, next to a drainpipe, which was tested by being tugged at with full force. Vincent, as it transpired, had invented a mountaineering game called 'roof-walking': in the evenings they'd climb house fronts in the city centre, walk along gutters and jump from house to house. If you didn't dare go any further or you fell you were out, the winner was the person who kept going the longest. There were frequent close shaves. Paul decided to join in and was the second or third to drop out. In the growing group watching the manoeuvres from street level, he learned more about Vincent – that he was a serial monogamist with a sell-by date of two months per relationship; that he only had to bend down during a mountain ramble and he'd find a semiprecious gem; that in response to a stupid question he'd bitten a frat boy on the nose (which Paul found rather priggish); that at six a.m. in a taxi-drivers' café he'd announced to two heroin dealers that 'And I will never grow so old again' was the most beautiful line in the history of music. From that first moment onwards Paul was impressed, not so much by Vincent's actions or the stories in which he featured but by his lack of hesitation, the complete ease with which Vincent moved and conducted himself. In the weeks that followed he repeatedly got the impression that he was nothing more than a goody two shoes country cousin.

Vincent opened a plastic bag which he'd removed earlier from his case.

'Hungry? We'd better start now otherwise we'll never get through all this.' He held up a packet of sandwiches and said that his mother had pressed all kinds of things on him before he left, as if he were going on a school trip. He'd asked her if she was going senile. 'As she sees it,' he said, 'I'll stay eight years-old until I get married. Wouldn't surprise me if she's spread them with Dairy Lea. Or peanut butter.' He was interrupted by a voice coming from hidden loudspeakers – a perfunctory welcome on behalf of the train personnel. Passengers were urged – in three different languages – to read the safety instructions and to visit the buffet car which had **** (incomprehensible) and coffee on special offer, they were urged to have a pleasant journey, and promised that 'you will feel like a king in the Eurostar'.

'Then a piddling little king, even the trains in Tokyo are roomier than this.' Vincent stretched out his legs into the aisle and bit into a pear. Paul remembered Vincent's claustrophobia; he hated long tunnels, they had once taken a sixty kilometre detour in Norway because of a tunnel Vincent considered 'unsafe'. Did he dare go under the Channel then? Or was that the point, another victory?

Paul heard the woman next to him sigh. She'd fallen asleep and was beginning to capsize with the train's jolts. Her shoulder touched his from time to time, causing him to feel her body heat through the thin layers that separated her candy pink skin from his own – and then she'd tilt, swaying through all her joints like a creaking ship, back to where she belonged.

'But I say,' Paul began, as he shifted position, 'what was in that newspaper then?'

'Ah,' Vincent replied with his mouth full. He straightened up. 'Front page.'

Paul picked up the paper and at the same time the window next to his head was almost shaken out of its frame. A train whizzed past from the other direction. Paul saw his face reflected in the window like an apparition and thought he looked as young as Vincent. And Martin and Lotte? He found it difficult to imagine them as any different than the last time he'd seen them years ago. When the last carriage was whisked away from the view outside like a curtain opening, he continued to look at the Belgian or perhaps French countryside above which a few solitary creamy-white clouds floated. Was it because he wasn't married, didn't have any children, had never had a normal job, that he still felt like an adolescent? He still found it ludicrous when he was addressed as 'sir'. In his own eyes he was just as healthy, strong and sharp-witted as he had been when he was eighteen. Recently he'd imagined he was approaching an abyss; that living was terribly risky; that at any moment he might disintegrate – but it was never more than a notion, yielding and distant. A ten house village swept by, the sun's reflection rushing along a stream stabbed the horizon. A warm glow began to travel through his body, he became singularly and acutely conscious of the slight rocking of the train and the grimy upholstery of the chair he was sitting on, of the gentle touch of his neighbour's shoulder and now there was a new smell too: nail polish. He lifted up the newspaper but didn't read what was written.

Because there it was. He suddenly saw it, straight through the paper. He reached out in front of him as if a door were about to close, right into the heart of the moment – he saw himself pushing off and jumping. The rope he was attached to was too short; he was pulled on his axis and missed, his hands grasping at emptiness, for a soundless second he swam with his arms and legs through the air and crashed full force against a ridge, slapping the air out of his lungs. Between his feet he could see her body tumbling beneath him, in a translucent hall full of shiny organ pipes and the roar of meltwater. He screamed but couldn't hear himself. A bubble of coldness welled up from the depths and enveloped him.

Yes – he had dreamed about it again last night. He had awoken in shock, he remembered that too. For twenty years he'd been dreaming of that one moment, with obstinate regularity.

It had been as beautiful a day as today – sun on your face, a quilt of silence over the landscape, the permanent suggestion that something else, something unimaginably peaceful lay behind the blue dome of the heavens. But Vincent wasn't there, he thought. He had seen Vincent later that evening and it had been chaos and everyone had talked at once. Had they talked about it again after that? No, of course not – he had made a promise. And another thing – there were matters you preferred to keep Vincent out of, he didn't know why exactly but sometimes even Vincent's presence could be oppressive. Why? Because – even Martin had said this – when he was around there'd be instant discussions and competition hanging in the air, the feeling that you had to prove yourself. Nothing was just casual with Vincent.

His gaze returned from the past, the letters on the newspaper shrunk into focus. He read the headline and then all of the accompanying article. Finally he held the paper further away and said, 'Why not? I'd be interested.'

Immortality Within Reach, it read. An American professor claimed that science could offer mankind eternal life. So this was the world news today. Not a natural disaster, not war but this, at first glance the only news they could find.

'I'm certain you'd regret it,' he heard Vincent say. Paul let the paper drop.

'Don't even think about it, pal,' Vincent said. 'Every day another meal, every day getting dressed, every day all those things that are already annoying – and then for all eternity? Unbearable!' He put the core in a sandwich bag, took out a handkerchief and began cleaning his hands meticulously. Paul wanted to say something – that actually he was becoming a little Japanese – but suddenly noticed that the front page of the paper the French couple were reading also announced La vie éternelle. The paper descended and he was stared at by two owls. He looked away, outside, to a moment from long ago – on his way to Martin's room on his bike. Their university town, a luminous morning in May. And there, in a fancy-free minute spent waiting at a jingling level crossing, the sensation that that minute would never end; a sensation that crumbled once he put his foot on the pedal, but the shock that had gone through his body then continued to vibrate now. Twenty – he'd been twenty, half his life ago. Just turned twenty and a year with the climbing club and that single moment on his bike had defined him – at least how he considered himself to be now: a person who sometimes did not exist when he was alone, or only as senses – pure receptiveness, perception – and only returned to being Paul, Paul van Woerden, when he came into contact with others, like now with Vincent. He laid his arm along the ledge under the window and felt cool air from the narrow grey grid streaming through his fingers. The train devoured the landscape at high speed. In the distance crows flocked above a sloping field – and yes, this alone, the thought fluttering up in him, this alone was a reason to embrace it with open arms: for a sky with tumbling birds and the liberating sensation of hurtling through such an exotic rolling landscape.

'When will we get that far?' Vincent asked. 'That American gives a date, doesn't he?'

Paul looked in the paper. 'In... about twenty years, he reckons.'

'But that's appalling!' Vincent laughed. 'Then we'll be about sixty. Instead of a young god you'll be stuck as a middle-aged feller – too old to have a proper go at climbing the Himalayas or have fun with healthy young girls, but too young not to feel sorry about it. Oh how you'll enjoy your eternal life!'

'Maybe I will,' Paul said. 'Once you're immortal everything will just be a question of time. Sooner or later you'll experience amazing inventions – like the possibility of living in a young body again. Or in an older body but with the capabilities of a young god, if you'd prefer that.'

Vincent's lower lip jutted out. He turned his knees in the aisle, put his case on his lap, flipped open the lock, pushed his hand under his laptop and Paul was struck by the thought that, just as he

couldn't escape his fellow passengers for the duration of a train journey, he'd be stuck with Vincent for the rest of his life. And with
Lotte, and Martin. The train took a long bend, his neighbour tipped
away from him, the sun's searchlight roved across Vincent's face
again. Now Vincent seemed like a scientific nomad more than anything else – the combination of self-mockery and self-satisfaction
and his way of acting as though he was accustomed to stepping onto
a continental flight each day with a trade publication under his arm.
And at the same time you suspected that there were entire areas
(classical music, literature) which, under the pretext 'I don't have
time anymore', he had left fallow for years.

Vincent got out of his seat again and, aiming between the French
newspaper and Paul's neighbour, tossed Paul a carelessly folded and
torn bluish map. Paul caught it and opened it, first in part and then
completely.

'Ah,' he said. He looked up. 'Where did you find this?'

Vincent shrugged.

Paul returned to the map.

Excerpted from *Grip* by Stephan Enter,
published by Uitgeverij Van Oorschot, 2011, 3rd printing.

JAN-WILLEM ANKER

A Civilized Man

AN EXCERPT FROM THE NOVEL,
TRANSLATED FROM THE DUTCH BY BRIAN DOYLE

Prologue

Broomhall, February 1771

A tidy two-hundred and forty years ago, a five-year-old boy rambled deep in thought on Broomhall estate in the diminutive Scottish kingdom of Fife, several tens of kilometres north-west of Edinburgh, on the opposite side of the Firth of Forth, where Pictish tribes once battled one another with axes and spears, at more or less the same latitude as Yekaterinburg in the east and Fort Edmonton in the west, established thirty years later and presently the capital of the Canadian province of Alberta, but then nothing more than a huddle of tents flapping in the prairie wind.

He wasn't normally allowed outside, and never without supervision. But he had managed to evade his nursemaid's attention and was enjoying the brisk winter air. His name was Thomas Bruce, the second son of Charles Bruce, the fifth Earl of Elgin and the ninth of Kincardine, and his wife Martha Whyte, the only daughter of London banker Thomas Whyte, who had already passed prematurely. A raw February wind blew in from the west and whistled with such intensity that it drowned out the voice of the boy's mother calling him. It was only when the nursemaid, with her doleful old-rose face, suddenly grabbed his shoulder that Thomas realised he had to go inside.

His father and brother were both seriously ill. He was expecting his mother to reprimand him for being outside without permission, but instead she embraced him. She gave him the drawing he had made that morning and took him with her without saying a word. He didn't have to take off his jacket. A bed had been set up for his father in the rear drawing room where a window had been left slightly ajar. The wind forced its way in, like the breath of an evil spirit. A heavy dark-blue curtain bulged out every now and then. Fever had soaked his father in sweat. A portrait of his grandfather, a man with grey whiskers, hung above the bed.

'What's that strange smell, mother?"

'The leeches.'

'Where are they?'

'In a jar,' said the surgeon. 'Would you like to see them?'

'When will father be better?' The boy took his father's hand, which lay limp on the bedcover. It was strange that the fingers of a limp hand were always curved and never straight. Hands always wanted to grasp something.

His father opened his eyes. 'Where am I?' he asked, staring at the ceiling. He tried to sit up. The doctor and one of the servants lifted him under his arms and slipped three sturdy cushions behind his back. He had to let go of his father's hand. His own hands now felt warm and a little clammy.

'Can't you open the window wider? I insist you open the window wider.'

'It's open wide enough, your lordship. It's already desperately cold inside,' said the surgeon.

His father turned his head and started to talk, but Thomas didn't understand a word. He placed the drawing on the bed and took a step backwards.

'What's this?' said his father. A horrendous bout of coughing followed. He wiped his mouth with a handkerchief and picked up the large sheet of paper. 'Dearest boy. Did you make this beautiful drawing just for me?'

'Yes, father. That's you on your horse going off to hunt and that's Achilles at your side.'

'What's Achilles doing?' asked his father. His face was pale and his skin seemed parched and dry. The strange smell lingered.

'He's barking, father.'

'A very fine drawing, my boy, you're so good at it. I'm proud to have a son with such skills. Come a little closer.'

Thomas hesitated. He was afraid to approach his father. He sensed a pair of hands pushing him forward. His father tried to laugh, but started to cough instead. This coughing fit was worse than the last. Spatters of blood appeared on his handkerchief.

'Do you have a sore throat, father?'

'Yes, my boy, very sore. But it'll be over presently.' He paused for a moment and then said: 'I'll be going to sleep soon. No, not sleep, I'll be at rest, that's something different.'

Thomas looked at his mother's face. He had a sense that something important was happening, but he didn't understand what it was. He wanted to cry, tried his best, but it didn't work.

'You're sure to be better tomorrow, father,' he said.

'You have to listen carefully, Thomas. Your father's going to rest for a long, long time. Perhaps not today, but very soon.'

'I don't want you to rest for a long time.'

The tears now started to flow and he felt relieved. He threw himself on his father's chest, crumpling his drawing. His father held him tightly. He smelled of roots.

'Nor do I, boy, but I don't appear to have a choice. Will you be good to your mother and William?'

At that moment the door opened and a servant appeared with a large jug of water and three full glasses on a tray.

'Off you go outside. Go and make a nice drawing for William. I'm sure he'll be as delighted as me.'

'I don't want to make a drawing. I want to stay here!' he sobbed, holding his father even tighter.

'Listen to me, Thomas Bruce. Are you a big boy?' his father's voice was extremely calm and nothing like the voice of a sick person.

'Yes, father,' he peeped.

'Good, then behave like one and leave the room. I'm thirsty and I want a moment alone with your mother.'

Thomas slipped from the bed and took his mother's hand. She led him out of the room. The servant held open the door. The nursemaid brought him to the kitchen where a steaming bowl of vegetable broth awaited him.

A double funeral took place a week later. His brother William had passed away two days after his father. He didn't die of the same illness as his father. His father had gone down with fever after a day riding on the estate. No one understood why. There was no flu about. They used a strange and unusual word to describe what had taken William. What was that word again?

The church in Dunfermline was packed with people dressed in black. Black jackets and hats, grey faces. Some coughed now and then. The shuffle of countless feet. He too wore black. He picked a bit of fluff from his chest and blew it into the air from the tip of his finger. He sat in the front pew next to his mother, absent. The high walls of the church seemed to curve inwards at the top to form a roof. It seemed deep, only the other way round; the more he looked up, the more he felt he was about to fall upwards and crash onto a floor in the air.

He looked at his mother. Her face was almost completely hidden behind a black veil. Only her mouth was visible. She pinched her lips tightly as if she was sucking something. Her white powdered jaw gave way to an equally white neck with a dark collar. He stared at the veil in the hope that he might catch an unexpected movement in her eyes, a flicker, a glimmer of light. If I'm not allowed to see her eyes, he thought, then she too was going to die. Then he would be completely alone, the last of the family, the only survivor, as if there was a competition to see who would last longest.

He looked at the lines on the palms of his hands. His brother had had the same lines, a little bigger but the same. He looked at the enormous wooden crucifix. The man hanging on it was the son of God. He was so thin you could count his ribs. He was in pain. Someone had hammered a huge nail through his feet. That was the worst of it. Not the wretched, suffering head, not the hands and the bloody wound in his side, but the naked feet, one atop the other. As if it hurt even more than nailing each foot to the wood separately.

He wanted to run, but was afraid that his mother would get angry or start to cry. He turned towards her a second time. She stared ahead unmoved, her body stock-still, her jaws clamped a little firmer than before. Her lips had disappeared inside her mouth.

All at once he remembered the name of William's condition: croup. They claimed that it was very hard on your throat, so bad that you had trouble breathing. An aunt had told him it was something children got. He listened to his own breath. Breathed in and out, and again in and out. Maybe he would see William and his father if he held his breath. After half a minute, when he thought his chest was about to crack, he let out a juddering gasp. His mother placed her hand on his neck.

'Croup,' he said without making a sound. He formed the word with his tongue and teeth, but left out the air. He had been angry because they had refused to let him see his brother. The surgeon had told him it would be too upsetting, but in spite of his solemn promise to control himself his mother and the surgeon had stubbornly refused. He had run outside, onto the grass, bawling and screaming. He had picked up a stone from the ground and thrown it at the sheep. They had panicked and scattered.

Most of the darkly clothed people had already left by the time they reached the family tomb. His mother was there, and his uncle

Ailesbury. His uncle nodded and smiled. He looked away in time to
see a massive roof being slid over William's resting place. The drawing he had made for his brother, which he hadn't had time to complete, lay beside him in the dark. He looked at his mother. She was
holding his hand, and hadn't let it go from the moment they entered
the crypt of the church. Her face was still hidden. It was dark. The
flickering candles created a creepy atmosphere.

'Mother,' he whispered, 'my hand hurts.'

She let go of his hand and grasped his shoulder. He looked up and
saw her face under the veil. Her eyes were moist. Teardrops rolled
down her cheeks, one after the other, as if her eyes were tiny ponds
filled to overflowing by the rain. They still had to pray, which he
did, more fervently than ever before. His mother collapsed, fell forward onto her knees. Her hands flat against the dark tiled floor, she
uttered a piercing shriek.

'Mother!' he shouted.

She scratched the tiles like a black cat in its death throes. Uncle
Ailesbury helped her up. He led her away from the tomb, unsteady,
docile. Her hands and her knees were dirty. Thomas looked back
for a last time at the darkness they had left behind. It sent a shiver
down his spine.

'I'll be fine,' said his mother, tossing her head as if she was trying
to shake a fly from her hair.

Ailesbury stood beside him, held him tight and said gently:
'You're the earl now, Thomas. The family's fate now rests on your
shoulders. That's a huge responsibility for such a young lad. Be
strong, be good to your mother and make sure she wants for nothing.'

Back at Broomhall, Ailesbury encouraged him to play in his room,
but instead he sneaked outside and sat on the steps between the
white marble pillars. The sky was blue. A lonely cloud drifted past.
There was no warmth in the sun. He rested his hand on a pillar and
he picked at a vein in the marble until he was holding a splinter of
the stuff in the palm of his hand.

* * *

He could have stayed on the Acropolis for an eternity, but duty
and horse-flies tore him from his reveries. Added to that, Hunt had
returned to Athens with a new list of locations to be excavated.

Consul Logothetis warmly welcomed his guests into his home. His dining table was straining under a wealth of local delicacies. His cook had accounted for British tastes and held back on the garlic.

Lusieri praised the Athenian carriers who had been hired to bring valuable artefacts to the Piraeus, the city's port.

'You would think they wanted to clear the entire Acropolis, and as quickly as possible,' Hunt observed.

'Athenians are simply the best when it comes to heavy labour,' said Hunt.

'Very true,' Elgin responded.

'The poor beggars,' said Mary. 'I feel sorry for them, to be honest. Back and forth with all those precious objects, and they haven't a clue. They might as well be carrying mud or compost, for all they seem to care.'

Everyone turned to look at Elgin who roared with laughter. Mary picked a piece of fluff from his shoulder and said nothing. She rested her hand affectionately between his shoulder blades.

Lusieri said he was convinced that there were valuable fragments of marble buried on the north side of the Parthenon, left over from the Venetian bombardment.

'So why don't we excavate?'

'There's a problem. A Turk lives on the site and he has good contacts with the governor, the voivode,' said Hunt. 'They might even be family. You never know with those Turks.'

Elgin rubbed the mask covering his wounded nose. It felt tight in the heat. He grimaced and Hunt responded with a smile.

'We plan to dig on the very spot where the Turk's house is located. But I fear we're going to need a new firman if we want to demolish it.'

'We could buy it.'

'Of course, your lordship, and I assure you we've tried,' said Hunt. 'But the owner is and remains determined not to sell his property, in spite of the generous compensation we've offered him. Picture this: the man is of no importance whatsoever, no one in the world cares a fig if he lives or dies. But fate has elevated him unexpectedly to a position of power. The man has never had so much power in all his life, by God. Small wonder he seems set to drag out the situation for as long as he can.'

'Did you give the voivode a telescope?' asked Elgin.

'Absolutely, your lordship,' Lusieri interrupted. 'The man was in the clouds with it and thanked me profusely, and the British Empire too, till the end of time.'

The following day, Elgin, Hunt and Lusieri paid a visit to the voivode, who was sitting in his usual place on the Acropolis. The earl trudged briskly over the dusty roads and scuttled up the steep path with evident energy. When they reached the top, the voivode stepped forward to welcome the British authorities. When he caught sight of the imposing figure of the earl he turned pale. He tried to be as cordial as he could, but he found it hard to hide his unease.

After the obligatory exchange of politenesses, the voivode asked with a slightly hesitant voice: 'How can I be of assistance, Excellency?'

Lusieri translated his words into French.

'I'm delighted you ask,' said Elgin. He adjusted his mask and told his story, with Lusieri's Greek – he had, in the meantime, mastered the language – echoing in the background. The voivode sputtered a few half-hearted words of protest here and there, but found it impossible to intervene, in part because Philip Hunt consistently filled in the gaps in Elgin's convincing argument. The Turk's house had to be demolished, otherwise his lordship would have to take appropriate measures when he was next in Constantinople.

'It goes without saying that the British Empire is willing to offer respectable compensation to the man. The house is in such a crucial location, but the money will give him the freedom to move elsewhere, even on the Acropolis. Although I can't imagine why he would want to live on the citadel surrounded by relics he knows nothing about. Or is he perhaps a connoisseur?'

The voivode informed them that the man had a Turkish mother and a Greek father and had been allowed to live on the rock for that reason. 'The man is poor, but proud,' said the voivode. 'He has spent half his life in that house, and he built it with his own hands, without any outside help. The man is very attached to his home. I'm sure the earl understands. Why should I send him away?'

'Greek or Turk, hand built or not: the house has to go,' said Elgin.

'The house must be demolished,' Lusieri translated.

'Sometimes a house just has to go,' said Hunt.

Elgin slapped his forehead theatrically.

'Effendi,' he said, 'I completely forgot to present you with a gift on behalf of the British government, in gratitude and appreciation for the outstanding cooperation you have facilitated between us thus far.'

Elgin handed the voivode a handsome gold snuffbox. The voivode's face lit up.

'Tell his lordship that I am most grateful and that I give permission for the man's house to be demolished for the sake of British-Turkish friendship.'

Lusieri passed on the message. Elgin bowed, wished the voivode a fine day, and told him he was looking forward to an intensification of British-Turkish relations. The Turks were a great and glorious people.

Elgin told jokes on the way back and charged Lusieri to start demolition the following day. At that very moment the owner of the house passed by with a heavily laden donkey. The man was almost as thin as the creature at his side, was shabbily dressed, had a stubbly beard, and just enough teeth in his mouth to make himself understood when he spoke.

Lusieri triumphantly informed him about the voivode's decision. The man started to stamp his feet and curse. Lusieri told him he would be generously compensated by none other than Thomas Bruce, the seventh early of Elgin and the eleventh of Kincardine. Never, the man growled, it's not for sale. He then bowed to Elgin and drove his donkey up the dusty trail.

The Greek begged, badgered and belly-ached not to have to leave his house, but the voivode refused to relent. He had made his decision. In spite of his few possessions, it took him three days to empty the place and vacate it. He worked the donkey half to death and its lamenting bray become louder with each passing hour.

Mary rarely spoke to Elgin, although she often asked him in the evenings if there was anything she could do to help. His response was always the same: he appreciated her concern, but had sufficient staff. Besides, it was good for the children to have their mother with them. Mary nodded and said nothing. While she supervised matters in and around the house, Elgin supervised the destruction of another house. A couple of brawny Greeks pounded away at it with sledge-hammers until it was nothing more than a pile of dust and rubble.

The shattered remains of its white stone walls reminded him of a ruined cemetery. The porters swiftly cleared the site, leaving not a single trace of the house that had once stood there.

In the days that followed, excavation work was organised from dawn to dusk. Under Lusieri's supervision, every cubic centimetre was sifted and scrutinized. They dug a pit so deep that the men were able to work in the shade of its walls. But they found nothing but dirt. The former owner came to witness the early stages of the dig. He had growled and gloated and grinned inanely each time he left the Acropolis. Lusieri ignored him as did Elgin. They had no other choice.

At the end he came back to look one final time at the place in which he had lived for so long. He saw the hole in the ground, so deep that the diggers had to be supported as they worked on the rock. He burst out laughing at the sight, unrestrained, deep and thundering, from the very bottom of his lungs. Even the voivode frowned when he heard it. It resounded across the Acropolis, carried by the wind past the houses and temples. It was as if the man had waited his entire life to release this laugh, like a pampered animal; as if he had endured the most wonderful seasons, most cheerful moments, most hilarious jokes and stories in silence, all to be able to open his mouth at this unique moment in time. It was as if he was laughing at the whole world, or as if the world was laughing through this one man's mouth.

When he had finished his guffaw, Elgin said to Lusieri: 'Ask him what's so funny about a hole in the ground.'

The man answered with a hint of fatigue in his voice: 'Tell me first why you bought my house? It surprises me that you demolished it. I thought you might use it to house some of the workers or for storage. But you've destroyed it completely. Did the British earl come all the way to Athens just for this? To demolish houses?'

Lusieri answered that the earl had come to Athens for the sake of art, and that they had hoped to find valuable pieces and fragments of marble in the ground upon which the house had stood.

'Marble fragments, yes, I remember the marble fragments,' the man answered with a grin on his bearded face.

'You do?' asked Lusieri taking a futile swipe at a fly.

'You mean those marble curls and bits of face and limbs that are all over this place?'

Lusieri nodded.

'Of course I remember them,' the man laughed. 'I ground them to make mortar and used it to build the house that your earl has spent the last few days having demolished. Or did he have a go with a hammer himself?'

Lusieri was gripped by a pitch-black rage. Who gave this barbarian the right to grind antique masterpieces for cement?

'Do I need to ask what he said, Don Tita?' asked Elgin, joining the end of the conversation.

Lusieri shook his head. His cheeks were ablaze.

With a broad grin that formed a ghastly tear in his beard, the Turk said: 'I wish you every success in your search for valuable sculptures. Please thank his lordship once again for the money. I plan to use it to build my new house. It's enough to build three.'

He turned and disappeared from sight. Elgin suggested to Lusieri that they go and have a drink to celebrate the fiasco. Celebrating with a drink was always better than not celebrating.

Excerpted from *Een beschaafde man (A Civilised Man)*,
published by De Arbeiderspers, Amsterdam, 2012

Photo: © Stephan Vanfleteren

HANNA BERVOETS

Everything There Was

AN EXCERPT FROM THE NOVEL *ALLES WAT ER WAS*

TRANSLATED FROM THE DUTCH BY MICHELE HUTCHISON

DAY 91

I'm not completely sure who first called the new situation "the new situation", but I think it was Natalie. It must have been the eleventh or twelfth day, in any case it was after dinner. A half carton of school milk and a shortbread biscuit. That's what it was then.

"Can I ask you something," Natalie said that day, "how long do you think this is going to last? I mean – the new situation."

We all looked at her. Hours, afternoons, nights on end we'd talked about it. Then Kaspar suggested we prepare ourselves mentally and practically for a period of weeks or even months. I said we should wait first. Barry shouted out that the uncertainty was driving him mad and Leo said Barry shouldn't do that, go mad, because it wouldn't make the situation any less uncertain, just a bit more unpleasant.

Yes, Natalie knew what we thought, and that we knew that she knew was something she must have known too. Her question was not so much a question but a statement, a way to make us think about it. I looked at her legs. Natalie hadn't worn her high heels any more after Day 5. There were black smudges on her flesh-coloured tights. I wondered when the tights would ladder.

"I think you're trying to say that we're going to be here for some time," Leo said finally.

"But how long then, mummy?" Joeri asked. Natalie didn't respond.

For a while we all looked on silently as Joeri played with an empty school milk carton. He picked the flaps loose, blew it up and threw it at Leo. He caught the carton, "We don't know how long, man."

"But probably quite a long time," Kaspar said. He was talking to Joeri but we could all hear him. I think Natalie had given him a nudge at that moment.

"So," Kaspar said, "maybe it would be better if each of us had our own place."

"What do you mean by that?" Leo asked.

"There are plenty of empty classrooms," Kaspar said, "but we're all here in the gym. Why is that? Is there a logical reason for all of us to sleep in the gym?"

Kaspar looked only at Leo now. "No," he said, "I don't think there's any logical reason." And Kaspar smiled. His bushy eyebrows shot up, the triumphant smile of a person who had been proven right at the end of a long argument. There wasn't any argument. There wasn't any being proven right. Yet the smile seemed appropriate.

"I've been thinking about those classrooms too," Barry now said quietly. I nodded slowly as well.

I'd thought about those classrooms pretty often. As early as the fourth day, after yet another broken night caused by Kaspar's snoring, Joeri's tossing and turning, and the walking and bumping and moaning of anyone needing to go to the toilet and then narrowly missing or hitting my mat. The idea that we'd each have our own classroom had seemed more practical to me for a long time. But I thought I'd wait and see. Perhaps I'm the only one. Might seem odd if I want to sleep alone. And on day eleven or twelve it still was: odd.

"So," Kaspar said, "shall we share out the classrooms then?"

Leo nodded. "If everyone agrees."

"If we don't all agree can't we just divide the classrooms up amongst the people who do agree?"

"Yes, Kasper," Leo said, "that's true."

"I think we all agree, you know," Barry muttered. "Don't we?"

There are ten classrooms. Four upstairs, six downstairs. The biggest classroom, the one that had belonged to year 3, is downstairs. It seemed logical that Natalie and Joeri would get that one. But Joeri wanted the classroom with the table football.

"Hey, Joeri," Natalie said, "but you can still play table football if we sleep in a different classroom, can't you?"

Joeri shook his head. "What if someone is lying underneath it?"

Finally we decided that nobody would sleep in the classroom with the table football, so that everyone could play whenever they wished. This meant that at least one of us would have to take one of the classrooms on the second floor.

"I don't mind," Barry said. "But if I was the only one sleeping on the second floor, I'd actually have four classrooms to myself. That wouldn't be fair, would it?"

I nodded. I knew what Barry was hoping. Sharing out the classrooms had nothing to do with fairness, but everything to do with seeking approval. Collective satisfaction always beats moral standards.

Leon now nodded at Barry too. Natalie muttered something which sounded like "fine", but Kaspar said, "Maybe Kaylem wants to sleep upstairs too." He turned. "Kaylem, do you want to sleep upstairs maybe?"

As soon as we'd agreed on the classrooms — Kaylem and Barry would sleep upstairs, the rest of us down — the tablecloths became a matter of discussion. We had three. Discovered in a cupboard in the teachers' common room. The biggest sheet was also the thickest: a red velvet length of cloth, probably used for Christmas dinners. We already decided on the first night that Natalie and Joeri should have it. But then there were two left. Plastic sheets, printed with cars. Cars with eyes and ears. "I don't need one," Leo had said immediately. "OK," Kaspar muttered after that. "I'll be all right sleeping under my coat." And so Barry and I had taken the tablecloths. "We'll swap tomorrow night," we'd said, "promise!" But from then onwards, everyone had slept on their own mat, in their own place, under their own coat or tablecloth.

"Is everyone going to take their covers to the new classrooms?" Barry asked now.

Covers, I thought. He's calling tablecloths covers. The vocabulary of the new situation.

"Yeah man," Leo said, "you just hang onto your favourite duvets." Leo laughed, I looked at Kaspar. "OK?" Kasper shrugged. "If you want . . ." For a while it seemed as though Kaspar was going to say something else, so Barry jumped in, "Are we going to move tonight or tomorrow night then?"

The entire discussion lasted about an hour, I looked at the clock above the climbing frame on the wall.

During the early weeks, we didn't do anything without discussing it in detail. Our discussions reminded me of the kind of debates you have on holiday in the morning on the patio of a rented villa: let's go to the beach today because it might rain tomorrow. But if we go to the beach, shall we have lunch there or back at the villa? Because if we have lunch here we'll have to go to the supermarket first, and then we might as well get stuff for the barbecue as well, although the big supermarket might be better, but if we drive all the way to the big supermarket, we'll barely be back home in time for lunch, so let's go to the supermarket right now instead, then we've done that: who's coming with us? Who is going to drive? Is there still enough money in the jar?

In the new situation, our debates were quite similar. Although the subject matter was different. "Where are we going to have lunch?" was "What shall we eat first: the shortbread or the milk biscuits?" "Who's coming to the supermarket?" became "Shall we have one more look around all the classrooms?" And "let's go to the beach today because it might rain tomorrow" was now "let's grill that mouse now because what are we going to do if the lights go out."

Over the course of time, the number of discussions decreased. Perhaps because we began to run out of choices. In any case because there were fewer people.

I mentioned holidays just now. Maybe you don't understand.

The resorts, amusement parks, swimming pools with water chutes, the bungalows with an open fireplace: I don't know whether they still exist. And whether life will ever go back to meaning that you work for thirty weeks and then take two weeks off, and that in those two weeks you take a train or a plane to a place where you don't live but where they do have towels, and walk around there a bit, buy something, take photos for the people who aren't there with you, because you want them to know what you saw when they couldn't see you.

In addition to this, in order to really understand it – a holiday – you first have to know what work is. Work still exists in the new situation. But there was a time when everything could be work. Sleeping, eating, drawing or doing a cartwheel: as long as someone else paid for it. And there always was someone like that.

My work, for example, was that I'd sit in a small room on the third floor of a tall building with Barry and some others, talking about three dimensional animations of RNA mutations, then I'd spin round in my chair and spend the rest of the day staring at a screen full of hydrogen molecules, test subjects or inbred dogs. Sometimes I'd go outside for a while to watch others smoke. Sometimes I'd read a text full of tables which had been checked by at least five professors. And sometimes, very occasionally, I'd telephone one of those professors to find out whether they could express themselves clearly enough to participate in our programme.

Work also meant having weekends: two days during which I didn't drink my coffee out of paper cups but out of a mug. Then I'd meet up with people I didn't see during the week, to discuss the past weekdays while drinking from that mug. What I'd done during those days, the people would soon forget. But that didn't matter. I'd soon forget myself. And the old situation, full of telephones, internet, Facebook and dozens of other ways of sharing things, was set up for communal forgetting. That was better than forgetting on your own. Or so it seemed.

But maybe none of this means anything to you anymore. A mug. An inbred dog. Facebook. I would like to explain it all to you, yes, I'd like to tell you everything about a life in which holiday and work alternated and we Twittered in the evenings to say we were watching television. I'm not sure whether you want to know about it though. It might be painful to read about the old situation. So let me also tell you what there still is.

Today, the ninety-first day since the bang: Barry is still ill. When I took him his rations today I thought for a moment that he wasn't there.

It was dark and quiet, as though I'd gone into my own classroom. I turned on the light. Barry's bedroom – Barry calls his classroom "a bedroom" – was exactly as it had been the day before. Curtains closed, *The Brothers Lionheart* open, still on the first page.

When he set up the room, Barry had stacked the little chairs and tables. On the floor there's a blue square we cut from the lino downstairs, two plants in front of the windows, one on the left, one on the right. "Nice and symmetrical," Barry said, "they'd eat their hearts out at Elle Deco."

This afternoon the plants still looked healthy. But the tips of their leaves were brown. As though someone had dipped them in basecoat. A song from a film popped into my head.

Oh, painting the roses red
And many a tear we shed
Because we know
They'll cease to grow
In fact, they'll soon be dead.

The drawing we did with Joeri was still on the board. I drew a house, four flowers and a sheep. Joeri drew some matchstick men with spiky hair. He called them Bladebreakers and wrote names underneath: Hiro Granger, Ray Kon, Hillar. Barry had only drawn a sun. A sun wearing sunglasses.

"That's wrong," Joeri said, "the sun doesn't need to protect itself from itself."

"Yes it does, you know," Barry had replied, "everyone needs to protect themselves from themselves."

I stepped carefully into the classroom. Barry was lying on the teacher's desk, the thick red tablecloth covering him. There was just a bit of hair sticking out.

"Barr," I whispered, "how are you feeling?"

"Merel?" Barry groaned.

"Yes," I said and walked over to him. On the chair next to the table there were three mugs. Exactly where I had put them on previous days: in a row, teaspoons sticking up out of them. I put the mug I was carrying down next to them.

"How are you?" I asked again. Now the cloth began to move.

"Ill," Barry whispered, "still ill."

"But you have to eat," I said. "Here's your share."

Barry groaned. "No, no sorry, honestly, no love."

"How's it going today?"

I turned around. Leo was standing in the entrance to the classroom, his head just missing the top of the doorframe.

A few steps and he was next to me. "Hey," he said gently to Barry, "how's it going?"

Barry didn't speak, Leo pulled the cloth down a bit.

"Do you think he has a temperature?" I asked.

Leo rested his hand on Barry's neck: "You need to eat something, man." But Barry just groaned and pulled the covers back over his head.

Leo and I stood there together silently. And suddenly I saw that Barry had added something to the drawings on the blackboard. At the bottom on the right, in white chalk, all of a sudden our names. Not just mine, Barry's and Joeri's, the people who'd made the drawings. No, also Kaspar, Leo, Natalie, even Kaylem. I wondered what I was looking at. School register, film credits. Or memorial plaque.

Leo rubbed the covers. "I think we'd better just leave him alone." And he picked up all four mugs with one hand.

"Did he feel feverish?" I asked when we were back downstairs around the fire.

Leo didn't answer.

"Maybe it's something from the outside," I said. "When Lotteke left, Barry closed the door and he's the only one who is ill now."

"Yes," Leo said, "that's right."

He stared into the fire, the flames lit up his face and created shadows on it too: dark smudges danced over his temples.

"Do you think it's something from the outside too?" I asked.

"I don't know."

"But what do you think?"

Leo slowly shook his head. Before I could say anything, he pointed to the mugs from Barry's classroom.

"They're starting to go mouldy. We'd better share them."

Leo tilted a mug so I could see its contents: a layer of sticky rice with green spots. He used the tip of his little finger to scrape the green off the white. He wiped the mould onto a pencil, threw the pencil into the fire and looked again at the layer of rice. "I'll have this one." Then he indicated that Leo should take the portion we'd made today. "You take that one." He shared out the third portion with a teaspoon: a few grains for me, a few grains for him, and a few grains for the fourth, left over mug. "Kaylem!" Leo called. He stood up, "Kaylem, there's more food for you!'

And so day 91 was the day we got an extra portion. But that's not how I have written it up in Melissa's diary. In Melissa's diary, today is the day I discovered that you were coming. And now I've found out, I want to tell the story better. How things were and how it happened. Yes, everything right from the start.

I think this means that I love you already. Love is wanting to be known. And I want you to know everything about me. The difficult thing is that I don't know whether you'll love me or not. Once you know everything.

DAY 5

This is our theory now. There must be more people like us. People who have been trapped somewhere since the bang. At home, in supermarkets, fitness centres, or other buildings. It happened on a Sunday afternoon. There must be people trapped in churches.

Some of those people have less food at their disposal. In time they'll ignore the instructions. Go over to the window, open the curtains, finally even venture outside. And if going outside is possible, those people will find other people. People who will also go outside, and find other people who will find other people who will find other people, until people have been found who know how to get the internet working again.

Maybe we'll have been found as well by then. There are enough other people who know we are here. Our editors. Barry's boyfriend. The board of the school. Natalie's husband. Erik, he's called. And Erik would definitely come and get his wife and son if he was capable of it. But Erik hasn't come. And Lotteke hasn't come back yet. When she left the building, it probably wasn't possible to be outside. As long as nobody arrives, it still can't be. And we'll stay inside.

Of course, everyone could be thinking this way. All the people stuck in their homes, in supermarkets or churches might be thinking: we won't go out so long as we can't see anybody else. In that case nothing will ever happen. But the chance is small. Or in any case not big enough to take the risk. So we'll have to wait until we are discovered. Everyone agrees.

Yesterday morning, Kaspar said, "We need to build up some food reserves." He gave Barry a questioning look when he laughed. "Sorry," Barry said. "But 'food reserves' sounded so Chip'n'Dale all of a sudden."

"I'm just being practical," Kaspar said, more quietly now.

Leo laid his hand on Kaspar's shoulder, "And that seems very sensible to me."

In the context of the food reserves, we decided to systematically check all the rooms, cupboards and classrooms. Leo thought it would be most efficient to do this in pairs, but Kaspar wanted to go with the whole group. What I thought was: Kaspar knows the building, he must want to give us a tour. But Leo said, "Don't you trust us, Kaspar?" It sounded like a joke, but Kaspar didn't find it funny. "I do, it's not that," he said, "I really do trust you." He said it too emphatically.

I hated the idea that Kaspar didn't trust us, even though his suspicions might have been justified. If we'd have gone off in pairs, and Barry and I had found a muesli bar, we might have eaten it just the two of us. Because if seven people all took one bite, seven people would have nothing. If two people took four bites, two people would have something. Seven people nothing or two people something – it wasn't a difficult decision. If it was just the two of you.

Yes, dozens of experiments with monkeys and students have proved that altruism is egotism in sheep's clothing. We share because we hope that others will share with us. But at the end of the day it isn't about what we do. It's about what others believe we do. Perhaps that was why I didn't like it that Kaspar didn't trust us. If you don't believe that others are sharing, you won't share yourself.

Excerpted from the novel by Hanna Bervoets
Alles wat er was (Everything There Was),
published by Atlas Contact, Amsterdam 2012.

• As we went to press we learnt that *Everything There Was* by Hanna Bervoets, translated from the Dutch by Florian Duijsens, will be published on 3 February 2015 by e-publisher Frisch & Co, and available world wide from www.frischand.co and major ebook stores

BENJAMIN BURG

Restaurant
Des Arènes

A SHORT STORY
TRANSLATED FROM THE DUTCH BY HESTER VELMANS

This takes place at the time when I was working for Richard. As guest waiter, temp waiter, or whatever you want to call it, I was then working six days a week for Richard, who was drunk at least twenty days a month. Staff turnover was high, they'd stick it out for about a week and then wouldn't bother coming back.

Except me, I quite liked him and didn't care if he was sober or not, the most important thing was that I had something to do, and I didn't have to kill myself doing it, because at Restaurant des Arènes the joint was never exactly jumping. The only place that was ever busy was the tiny bar next door, that's where the regulars hung out, drinking with Richard, mostly on the house. After that, dining wasn't usually on the cards.

One evening I notice a man standing outside on the terrace, a child in either hand: on the left a boy around eight years old, on the right a girl, five or so. The man has his face pressed three inches from the menu posted in the glass case outside. Kids just stand there quietly, don't say a thing. Man takes two steps back and just as I'm thinking "We won't be seeing that one again", he steps back onto the terrace, children in tow, and asks if we have a table for him.

"I'll have a look," I say. "Did you have a reservation?"

"Sorry," he says, "sorry." He looks at the children, then at me.

"We're expecting a big group," I tell him, "but if you'd like to sit down right this minute, it's not a problem, come on in."

"Oh, good," he says, "that will be great."

I point him to a four-top against the wall.

"Have a seat," I say, and make a tour of the room to inspect the other tables. Then I walk through to the kitchen, where our cook, an Algerian boy, sits smoking a cigarette.

"Customers," I say.

He doesn't look up from his cell phone.

"Customers," I say again. Then wander over to my usual place behind the counter, put on something by the Gypsy Kings, who are from around here originally, or so I've heard.

"Something to drink?" I ask when I'm back at their table.

"Do you have anything nice in a burgundy?" asks the man, "But I mean something really good, not just any old bottle, a good, full-bodied, earthy wine, with a touch of the barnyard, but refined."

I gaze at him with raised eyebrows.

"And two cokes for the children," he says, "one with ice, the other without."

"Two cokes," I repeat.

I hand him the wine list and push my way through the curtain into the bar where Richard is holding court. There are four men and one woman in there, and on the counter a bottle of champagne in an ice bucket which I can already tell you won't wind up on anyone's tab. Neither will the next one.

When Richard catches sight of me, he waves vaguely at the bar and announces, to the others, "My friend." They glance in my direction. I give him the drinks order. When I go to pick up the tray, I feel his warm clammy fingers on my wrist. He looks at me as if he was going to ask me something but has forgotten what it was, and lets go.

As I set the cokes down before the kids, the man is talking to them, leaning forward, his head hunched between his shoulders, like some big bird perched on a branch. He pushes the wine list toward me, points at something.

"We don't sell that one by the glass," I say. "Maybe a half bottle."

"Don't bother," he says. "Just bring me the whole bottle." He squints up at me sideways. "A bottle of this one. Do you recommend it?"

"I don't know that one," I say.

"A full-bodied, earthy wine? Yet refined?"

"I can ask my boss."

"If you'd be so kind," he says. "Thanks."

I push my way through the curtain again, wait two seconds, then return to my table and tell him the boss says it's an excellent choice.

"I'm glad," says the man, "Glad to hear it."

The restaurant has eighteen tables inside and twelve out on the terrace, enough to seat a hundred. It's slow tonight. Tuesday nights are always tough, but tonight there is even less going on than usual. If we weren't expecting that large party, we might as well have closed up for the night; it would save Richard a ton of money.

But Richard doesn't pay too much attention to money. I've made enough dough in my lifetime, he says, and blown it too. Blown all of it, ha, ha, ha, he says. It seems he used to have a restaurant in Paris that was very popular. Richard knew everyone and everyone knew Richard. Until five years ago. Then he wound up here, with his two little girls — big girls now. Another restaurant, but different this time, simpler, more in line with the way he wanted to live his life now. I don't know what he was expecting, but I have the feeling it never got off the ground exactly, that new life.

The man hasn't stopped talking from the moment he sat down with his kids at the table along the wall. He just keeps on talking, and the kids never say anything back in response. The boy is drawing pictures on the paper placemats with the black pen I gave him, the girl is playing with some little plastic toys from McDonald's. They're both looking down, and never stop what they're doing, but from the way they hold their heads cocked sideways over the table, I think I can tell they are listening. I turn the music down a bit and cool my heels behind the counter, two tables away from them.

"Remember this," I hear. "Never forget. It's very important."

The man has something to tell the children, that much is obvious. From time to time he'll ask a question, and then the children will glance at him, but before they have a chance to answer, he's started talking again.

When I bring them their food, shoulder of lamb for the man, hamburgers and fries for the kids, they are quiet for nearly fifteen minutes.

"That was excellent," says the man, dabbing at his mouth with his napkin. "Would you please tell the kitchen? Really very good. Don't you agree?" he asked. The children nod, not looking up from their plates.

"They thought it was excellent too," he says.

"I'll let the chef know," I say.

I clear the table, carry the plates into the kitchen, where the chef is lolling in front of a small TV. When I come back into the dining room the man is hunched even lower over the table, and I notice that his nose is very large compared to the rest of his face, and that his eyes are sunk rather deep into their sockets, which does make it look as if there's some huge bird hovering over the table, an eagle, or a vulture.

The children are still busy playing, the boy's felt tip scribbling fiercely across the paper, the girl pushing her toys back and forth along the edge of the table. And the man won't stop talking.

"Of course Mama was lovely," I hear him say. "But Julie is very sweet, really, very sweet. Don't ever forget that. Julie likes you a lot, I'm sure of it, I want you to know that. Never forget, she likes both of you, a lot. And she'll always be there for you, no matter what..."

It's as if the man is saying the same thing over and over, using different words perhaps, but it's essentially the same message the kids are being given to hear.

If you found yourself having to wonder about the life story of every customer, you might as well go get a job in a loony bin. It's just as well, really, that you don't need to know everything. And, honestly, it's none of my business. I come, I do my job, and I leave. The rest is no concern of mine. Where my customers are from, what makes them tick, where they're off to afterwards, I don't know, and I don't care to know either. I have enough problems of my own.

Three months before the man and his kids walked into my restaurant, I was living in a room just ten feet by twelve looking out on a blank wall, furnished with only a mattress and a wooden chair, empty pizza boxes all over the floor. Until the day I decided it couldn't go on like that any longer. Until the day a friend I had known since elementary school and one of the few people I'd stayed in touch with over the years, declared that enough was enough, that if I went on like that I would wind up in the gutter — as if that weren't the case already — and invited me to come and live with her and her husband for a while. It wasn't an invitation, it was a command, she said.

So that's where I'd landed, and it was the same friend who had taken me to Des Arènes one night. There I met Richard, who was already pretty far gone by the time we arrived at nine o'clock, but who despite or perhaps because of that immediately took a shining to me.

"You have suffered a great loss," he said, "I can see that."

There was no need to say anything, because Richard didn't give me the time to respond.

"A woman," he said, "a girlfriend, a fiancée. Gone. Walked out, bye-bye. Address unknown, nothing left behind, not even a note."

He stared past me out the window where at that moment it was too dark to see anything, and went on, "And you don't know why. You have no idea."

I didn't know how to react. Richard was drunk, to be sure, but not unpleasantly so, he didn't do that insistent, in-your-face thing that makes drunks come off as threatening, although I did think he was being rather direct, for a Frenchman.

The truth was that I'd had nobody walk out on me that way. I hadn't been left by any girlfriend. I tried to make that clear to Richard, but that night he refused to hear it.

"And now you've sunk to the bottom," he said after a minute's silence. "As low as you can go. And you're asking yourself what's next."

Just as I decided I'd had enough of hearing all these revelations about my life, an acquaintance of Richard's walked into the bar and Richard allowed himself to be dragged over to another table.

"It's his own story," said my friend, "you do understand that, don't you? I don't know the details, but I do know that Richard had a wife, the mother of his two daughters, they were married for fifteen years. One day, she suddenly walked out on him with no warning, leaving him with those two kids, twelve and fourteen at the time."

When we were leaving I shook Richard's hand.

"I know your whole story," he said, "you can't keep anything from me. And if you need a job, I can always use good people."

A few days later I went back to the bar and told him I needed money and would like a job.

"Fine," said Richard, "you can start here in the bar, that way I can keep an eye on you, and then when you have some idea of how the place works, you can move over to the restaurant."

For the first few weeks Richard and I ran the bar together, and then I was promoted to the other side of the curtain. My shift started at seven p.m. and ended at one a.m.; sometimes when there weren't any customers we'd close up earlier, but often — just about always on the weekends— the doors wouldn't be locked until three a.m. and I'd have to enlist the help of one of the remaining customers to see that Richard got home safe.

It wasn't hard to love the man. Everyone loved Richard, some simply because he was a lovable guy who would never harm a fly, others because he sang beautifully when he was pissed, and some of the regulars for the reason I've already mentioned.

I believe that when it came right down to it only Richard knew the reason for his almost chronic inebriation, or maybe even he didn't know, but I do find it hard to believe that it was just on account of the wife who had walked out on him. No matter how beautiful or special she may have been, it seemed to me that there had to have been more to it for a man to lose himself that way.

I thought of his daughters, the girls he had brought with him when he'd moved south when they were still relatively young, but who now had boyfriends and were going their own way. They too were slowly but surely disappearing from his life. The older one was no longer living at home, the younger was about to go off.

And even though I'm willing to accept that these things had all played an important part, I think that there must have been some other, deeper sadness lurking somewhere inside Richard, which the departure of his loved ones had suddenly propelled to the surface, the way a submerged ball pops up out of the water when you take your hand away.

I, for my part, had never been left by a wife or a girlfriend, nothing in my life bore the slightest resemblance to the circumstances Richard had described on that first night. The only woman I could think of was my mother, who had died five years earlier. Of course I had been sad, but everyone who's ever had a mother knows that she won't be there some day; and knows, too, that there's no point mourning her forever.

And yet, from my dealings with Richard and from being around him on an almost daily basis, seeing him in his best moods and at his worst moments, both his ups and his downs (when he could burst into tears without warning), I was slowly beginning to understand why I, at twenty-eight, in the prime of my life, had whiled away my days doing absolutely nothing, in a room a hundred foot square, with nothing in it but a sink to wash myself in, subsisting on a diet of pizza margherita and quattro stagioni.

The reason was as simple as it was banal: you're born into this world, you die, and there's no one who'll stick it out with you in between. Some are better at handling it than others. Perhaps Richard called me a friend because he thought that we were cut from the same cloth in that regard — cloth of a flimsy sort to be sure, easily torn.

The man raises his bird head and waves me over to his table.

"We'd like to order a dessert," he says, "if we may."

I take a step back, gaze up at a spot somewhere on the ceiling and recite: "Crème caramel, nougat glacé, île flottante, mousse au chocolat, ice cream, sorbet..."

"What flavors ice cream, exactly?" asks the man.

I clamp one eye shut and continue: "Strawberry, raspberry, mint, vanilla, lemon, kiwi..."

"Just bring us a bit of everything, if it's not too much to ask," says the man. "The children like anything as long as it's sweet. Just bring us a nice selection of the sweet stuff, please."

A little later I heap their table with little plates, bowls and dishes, filled with every sort of dessert the Restaurant des Arènes has to offer that evening. It's the first time I see the children look up. The little boy has the same pale face as the man, the same eyes set deep into the sockets. The girl's face rounder, with the most wistful eyes I have ever seen. When I return to the table, it looks as if they've sampled just a couple of spoonfuls of every dish.

"It was excellent, thank you," says the man, getting up from the table. "We have had a delicious meal. The children too. An excellent evening."

"You're welcome," I say, and as they start toward the door I begin clearing the table. I gaze after them as they proceed across the terrace and into the street, the boy on his left, the girl on his right. The man himself somewhat hunched forward, as if he is tired and the children have to pull him along. Above them a dark blue sky. Then I return to their table. I pick up the empty wine bottle and gather the place mats with the boy's drawings of black houses, every house firmly crossed out in black.

Paul Starkey reviews

Beirut, Beirut
by Sonallah Ibrahim
Translated by Chip Rosetti
Bloomsbury Qatar Foundation
Publishing, Doha, 2014.
ISBN: 978-9992194522. Pbk, 263pp,
£10.28/ $17.99. Kindle £6.69/$10.76

Publishing in war-torn Beirut

Thanks largely to the translations of Richard Jacquemond, French-speaking readers have hitherto enjoyed a decisive advantage over their English-speaking counterparts in getting to grips with the works of Sonallah Ibrahim, one of Egypt's most distinctive contemporary authors. The last few months, however, have seen a sudden, and highly welcome, surge in the availability of Sonallah Ibrahim's writing in English translation. Following Robyn Creswell's retranslation of *That Smell* [*Tilka al-Ra'iha*] and extracts from *Notes from Prison* [*Yawmiyyat al-Wahat*], published by New Directions in 2013; a further selection from his prison diaries published in *Banipal 50*; and the reissue of Husam Aboul-Ela's's translation of *Stealth* [*al-Talassus*] by New Directions earlier this year, we now have a translation of another of the author's full-length novels, *Bayrut, Bayrut*, originally published in Arabic by Dar al-Mustaqbal in 1984.

The geographical setting of *Beirut, Beirut* is itself not without interest, for Egyptian writers in general have not been noted for their concern with other parts of the Arab world; and indeed, it is probably no exaggeration to say that, with the conspicuous exception of the Palestine-Israel dispute, Arab writers have, at least until recently, shown a certain reluctance to interest themselves in the problems of the region outside their own particular countries. Although the Lebanese war itself provides a proportion of the material for the

novel, however, this is by no means the novel's only concern, and problems of publishing in the Arab world (a subject on which the author could bring to bear significant personal experience) clearly emerge as one of the work's preoccupations. Sonallah's interest in the Lebanese Civil War indeed appears itself to have been initially sparked by the difficulties of publishing his work in Egypt, prompting him to visit Lebanon in 1979. Then, as now, the country enjoyed a reputation as one of the most liberal publishing centres in the Arab world, but for some four years had been in the grip of a complex civil war that was to last until 1990. Finding himself in the middle of the conflict, and in an attempt to understand what was happening, the author began to research and document the events around him, and it was this research that forms the basis for the present work.

Like many of the author's other works, *Beirut, Beirut*, though not an autobiography, is narrated in the first person, and contains obvious autobiographical elements. As with many of the author's other novels also, the 'plot' of the work as such is rather thin. The main events of the work revolve around the experiences of an Egyptian writer, who travels to Beirut towards the end of 1980 in the hope of finding a publisher for his controversial latest book. Arriving in the city on 7 November 1980, he meets an old friend from his revolutionary student days and is introduced to two fascinating, though very different, women: the idealistic film-maker Antoinette, and Lamia, the seductive wife of a potential publisher, 'Adnan al- abbagh. In pursuing his publishing possibilities, the narrator is drawn into a series of meetings and other encounters, which expose some of the complexities of the Beirut publishing scene, currently exacerbated by the civil war, as well as publishing problems in the Arab world more generally. At the same time, the writer also becomes involved in a second literary enterprise – the writing of a film commentary on the civil war itself – that draws him in a still more immediate way into the turmoil of current events in the region.

photo: Samuel Shimon

Sonallah Ibrahim

Meanwhile, the sexual chemistry between Lamia and the narrator has become increasingly evident as they banter light-heartedly about their differing Lebanese and Egyptian accents – though again, as often in Sonallah's works, frustration rather than fulfilment is the dominant romantic mode, and after a series of generally unsuccessful encounters, on both a professional and a personal level, the book closes with the narrator preparing to return to Cairo, his novel still unpublished.

Despite its non-Egyptian setting, readers already familiar with Sonallah's other fiction will recognise in *Beirut, Beirut* many of the themes and techniques that pervade his writing – not least, his intertextual approach to composition, which blends fact and fiction, incorporating into the author's own narrative real or invented documents from outside the text. By this means, as Chip Rosetti notes in his brief but pertinent Translator's Afterword, the work offers an outsider's window "into a historical event that is at once very familiar and increasingly distant" (p.344). Although this is by no means Sonallah Ibrahim's best novel (in my view, at least), like almost everything the author has written it represents an intriguing and distinctive addition to the corpus of modern Egyptian literature, and it is good to have it available in English in Rosetti's highly accomplished translation. Let us hope that the publishers can be persuaded to take on more translations of Sonallah's novels, so that English-speaking readers can enjoy the same access to this fascinating writer as those able to read in Arabic or French.

FORTHCOMING ISSUE

Contemporary Fiction from Oman

Riyam Roundabout, Muscat, Oman, photo Samuel Shimon

Susannah Tarbush reviews

Gertrude
by Hassan Najmi

Translated by Roger Allen
Interlink Books, Northampton, MA,
USA, 2014. ISBN 978-1-56656-971-2.
Pbk, 282 pp, £8.70/$15.00. Kindle
£6.86/$11.03

From Tangier to Paris

In her 1933 bestseller *The Autobiography of Alice B Toklas*, the legendary gay American writer and art collector Gertrude Stein mentions how she and her lifelong partner Alice got to know a young Moroccan during a visit to Tangier in 1912.

"We had taken on a guide, Mohammed, and Mohammed had taken a fancy to us," writes Stein. "He became a pleasant companion rather than a guide and we used to take long walks together and he used to take us to see his cousins' wonderfully clean arab [sic] middle class homes and drink tea. We enjoyed it all."

Moroccan writer Hassan Najmi takes this encounter as the inspiration for his engaging and absorbing novel *Gertrude*, first published in Arabic in 2011 by Al-Markaz al-Thaqafi al-Arabi.

The novel opens with the elderly Muhammad on his hospital deathbed. The only other person present is a young writer and poet, the unnamed narrator of *Gertrude*. This close friend agrees to Muhammad's final plea, that he write the story of Muhammad and Gertrude.

In reality Muhammad never again saw Gertrude and Alice after their visit to Tangier. But in

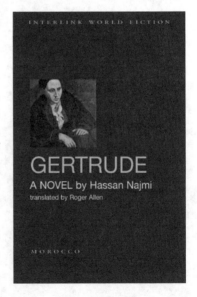

Hassan Najmi

Najmi's novel, the lesbian Stein loses her virginity to Muhammad
at the Hotel Villa de France. She invites him to visit her and Alice in
Paris, where she has lived since 1903 and where she is mentor and
patron to numerous pioneering artists and writers. Muhammad
pines for Gertrude and eventually takes her up on her invitation and
travels to Paris. He moves into a rooftop room in the apartment at
27 rue de Fleurus where she lives with Alice and resumes his passionate affair with her: "He touched her shoulder, her back, her
waist, her breasts, everywhere on her body, and she writhed like a
rhinoceros roaming wild in the bush." Alice tries to cope with having
to share her lover, but "she still cannot understand why her companion should agree to put her body in the hands of this Moroccan
man to play with, just as though it were on a table for dissection".

Muhammad mingles with the artists and writers of the day at
Gertrude's Saturday evening salons, the walls covered with paintings by the artists. They include Picasso's famous 1905-06 portrait
of Stein, reproduced on the cover of *Gertrude*. In his old age Muhammad often told the narrator stories of his time with Gertrude, and
of the famous artists and writers he had met through her, but the
narrator never fully believed these tales. On his deathbed Muhammad gives him papers, cuttings and faded photographs to help him
write about him and Gertrude.

After Muhammad's death, the narrator is distracted by his sacking from his teaching job after a strike, and his move to Rabat to work as a journalist. When he at last examines the material Muhammad had given him he is thrilled to realise that Muhammad's stories about Gertrude and her circle were based on truth. The narrator is determined to find out all he can about Stein. He is helped by a US Embassy information attaché, Lydia Altman, who gets him books by and about Stein and photocopies material for him. Lydia is an attractive Afro-American with a forthright manner. When at the end of his first visit to her office he thanks her for her help and for being very warm with him, she surprises him by replying: "How do you know I'm warm? We've never slept together!" Before long, the two are in a physical relationship, with the narrator giving little consideration to the fact that he is a husband and father. "At times I found it hard to distinguish between Lydia and Gertrude," he says.

Najmi, born in 1960, is a leading Moroccan poet, novelist, journalist and educator and has twice been president of the Moroccan Writers Union. In 2007 he was elected president of Morocco's House of Poetry, of which he was a founder in 1996. A number of Najmi's poems have appeared in earlier *Banipal* issues, as has an essay on the poet Adonis. An excerpt from *Gertrude*, translated by Nancy Roberts, was published in *Banipal 43*. Najmi's gifts as a poet, and his descriptive powers, illuminate his prose fiction. He wonderfully evokes Tangier, Rabat, Paris, and the south of France where Gertrude has a house. He handles the large cast of characters with ease, and the main characters are depicted with nuance and depth.

Roger Allen has produced a finely-tuned, crystalline translation that is a pleasure to read. Allen is Emeritus Professor of Near Eastern Languages & Civilizations (Modern Arabic Literature) at the Middle East Centre of the University of Pennsylvania's School of Arts and Sciences. He has translated many Arabic novels, and won the 2012 Saif Ghobash Banipal Prize for Arabic Literary Translation for his translation of Moroccan author Bensalem Himmich's *A Muslim Suicide* (Syracuse University Press 2011).

Naimi has a playful approach, and there are echoes of *The Autobiography of Alice B Toklas* in his novel's freewheeling, non-linear structure. He takes numerous liberties with chronology, for example referring to Anaïs Nin and Henry Miller as lovers in Paris years before they actually were, but this matters little.

The aged Muhammad emerges as a fascinating, endearing person in the milieu of writers, artists and intellectuals in Tangier. He still suffers pain from his memories of Gertrude, and of his cousin Bakhta whom he had intended to marry but who married someone else during his absence in Paris. Gertrude had taught him to make notes and write on a daily basis, but while her writing was published his remained in drawers. In Tangier he called himself "a retired writer" or "formerly a writer" – but no one had read anything he wrote. He was however a treasury of oral stories, on which other writers drew.

The central conceit of *Gertrude* – that the celebrated eponymous lesbian had a sexual relationship with a young Moroccan – could be too much for some readers to accept. But even those who start out sceptical may well be drawn into a magical and highly original work of fiction.

Margaret Obank reviews

Tales of the Marvellous and News of the Strange

Translated by Malcolm C Lyons
Introduced by Robert Irwin
Jacket Illustrations by Coralie Bickford-Smith

Penguin Classics, November 2014. ISBN 9780141395036, Hbk, 496pp,
£25.00/$21.78, Kindle £13.99

First English translation of a 1,000-year-old Arab fantasy collection

Congratulations to Penguin Classics for bringing to English readers this amazing collection of ancient tales. The first words of Robert Irwin's introduction reveal the exceptional treat that awaits them: "Here are wonders and mysteries indeed."

The manuscript of the eighteen anonymous tales was found in a library in Istanbul by the great German Arabist Hellmut Ritter in the early 1930s, which itself is a tale waiting to be told. A German translation of these tales was published in 1999, and now for the first time they appear in English translation by Malcolm C Lyons, who also co-translated the recent Penguin Classics edition of *The Arabian Nights*, edited and introduced by Robert Irwin (they make a terrific team). The tales read so fluently and beautifully that they easily transport the reader into the fantastical realms of the imagination.

Six of the tales are included in

The Arabian Nights collection, while the other twelve are completely new. And just as in *The Arabian Nights*, the titles are glorious, like this example: "The Story of Sul and Shumul with Reports and Poetry, and How Shumul Was Abducted, As Well As What Ordeals Her Cousin Sul Faced and How the Two Were Reunited. It Is a Marvellous Tale." The tales are often stories within stories, with kings or emirs requesting a poor man tell a story to calm them, ranging from strange meetings with jinn and monsters of the sea and land, to travels, voyages to Basra and China, searches for lost ones, tests of love, treasure hunting, love stories, grief over loss of loved ones, terrible sorrows and lamentations. All human emotions and desires are freely expressed in the tales, along with torture so that "things would become clear" – they tied one man "to a whipping post and gave him three hundred lashes", and then gave him another three hundred!

A striking feature of the collection is the diverse range of religious sensibilities and environments, which reflect the reality of the multi-religious and multi-ethnic area of the Fertile Crescent, where the stories seem to be set. There are sorcerers and sorceresses, hermits, idol temples, churches, mosques, Muslims, Christians, jinn, gods of the sea and land. A number of the stories begin with a dedication such as "In the Name of God, the Compassionate, the Merciful," and end with praise, as in "Praise be to the one God and blessings be on the best of His creation, our Master Muhammad and his family", while others just start their tale and end with a simple statement, such as "This is the complete story".

The final tale of marvels is "The Story of Mahliya and Mauhub and the White-footed Gazelle. It Contains Strange and Marvellous Things". In it, a hermit tells a story to an emir of the adventures of princess Mahliya, who later becomes a rather tyrannical queen, and of how both she and the prince Mauhub meet in Jerusalem, where she had been sent "to do what the other royal children did", and where, on reaching maturity, he had also been sent by his father, who was descended from Nebuchadnezzar, "to be baptised in the font of the church in Jerusalem" and then "taken to Bethlehem".

This story in particular is noted by Robert Irwin in his introduction for its "sheer wild inventiveness", "with its jumbling of Muslim, Christian and pagan beliefs and rituals". He writes that it "has a mechanical vulture, visionary dreams, conversation with a pagan god, magical transformations, thrones of wrath and of mercy, an enchanted gazelle, a herder of giant ostriches, a fortress guarded by talismans, a crocodile with pearls in its ears, the sacrifice of virgins to the Nile and much else". The prince and princess fall in love, and enjoy nights of wine and lute-playing, with Mahliya following a circuitous route of disguise (somewhat in the manner of Rosalind in *As You Like It*) and trickery, while playing to the affections of Mauhub, who is enthralled by a sorceress, but eventually rescued by the resourceful Mahliya.

The merging of fact and fantasy is taken as read. What is true and what is fantasy are not up for discussion. The storyteller and the reader slide effortlessly from one to another creating the ultimate realm of imagination. As a publisher, and reader, of contemporary Arabic literature in English translation, every one of these tales reminds me that many Arab authors today are doing the very same thing, blurring the line, actually cancelling it out, and in doing so creating narratives that are well grounded in both worlds, and that therefore make the reader reflect deeply – authors such as Emile Habibi, Zakaria Tamer, Fadhil al-Azzawi, Bensalem Himmich and Waghdi al-Ahdal, to name just a few with works in English translation.

While most of the tales' leading figures are emirs, kings, queens, princes or princesses, qadis or governors, who all live in magnificently sumptuous palaces, surrounded by gold, silver and precious jewels, and dressed in fine robes, in the main the storytellers within the tales are poor, disfigured or disabled, and handsomely rewarded with gifts, including banquets with "trays of gold and silver . . . on which were glasses of fine crystal containing wine of indescribable excellence".

These tales are more than 1,000 years old but in some ways they have a very contemporary feel to them. With little or no characterization of the main actors, except for descriptions of their beauty, clothes, jewels and palaces, there's an uncanny similarity to today's never-ending reporting on celebrities, their clothes and mansions by the popular news media.

Likewise, the violence in the tales, the brutality, the raping, bloodletting, knifings, killings by the hundreds and crucifixions, all recounted with a kind of matter-of-fact relish, recall the present-day proliferation of violent films and PC games, not to mention the unending wars going on around us in the real world.

A notable aspect in some of the tales is the portrayal of princesses or queens as immoral, scheming, duplicitous, treacherous, untrustworthy and seductive – reminiscent of the portrayal of Eve in many eyes, through the ages, though erroneously, "as the original cause of all evil". In Tale Seven, "The Story of Arus al-Ara'is [Bride of Brides] and Her Deceit, As Well As the Wonders of the Seas and Islands", the king is grief-stricken when his beautiful young daughter falls sick and dies. A blind man tells him he has "an excellent tale" that will console him and "lead him to hate scheming and treacherous women and girls", and so begins to recount the amazingly complex and extraordinarily brutal and jinn-powered adventures of Arus al-Ara'is, who was "like a full moon, the most beautiful that had ever been seen, with jewels and magnificent robes, and the splendour of her beauty illumined all that was around her", but was up to no good and destroyed everything and everyone around her.

This volume of "Tales" and "News" is a magnificent achievement. It comes complete with a very useful glossary and its pages bound by beautiful illustrations, on both outside and inside covers, of an unusual tree of life. Highly recommended.

Robin Ostle reviews

WARFARE AND POETRY IN THE MIDDLE EAST

Edited by Hugh Kennedy

I B Tauris, London, 2013.

ISBN: 978-1780763620. Hbk, 240pp, £62/$81.29

The poetry of heroism and hell on earth

Warfare is much on the collective mind at the moment, especially in this, the centenary year of the Great War that was to end all wars. Forlorn hope! A hope that dies on a daily basis crushed by the remorseless beatings of the narratives of conflict from the Ukraine to the Levant. The Middle East has an unenviable record in the history of warfare and none more so than in recent times: it was part of the theatre of war in the two global conflicts of the 20th century, and since 1918 there has been scarcely a decade in which military conflict in its different dimensions has not brought untold suffering and sacrifice to its usually random victims. A crucial influence in maintaining warfare as somehow part of what a population accepts on the part of any country is the manner in which it is commemorated, one might almost say celebrated. Wars and battles are remembered, often annually, through marches, demonstrations of military hardware, music and moving speeches, which may involve poetry. These are public performances: they celebrate the valour and heroism of the survivors and the victims, and occasionally the enemy is accorded an honourable place in these rituals. They are undoubtedly moving and cathartic occasions for those who participate in them, but few if any are exhortations for "no more war!". Rather they are ritualized preparations for the next round of hostilities.

Poetry and warfare have been interlinked throughout recorded history, and poetry has played its full part in the processes of honouring the valour of heroes and their leaders. But the best of this

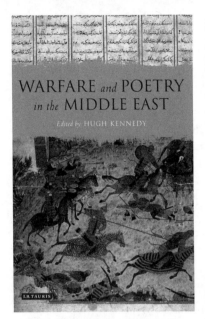

WARFARE and POETRY
in the MIDDLE EAST
Edited by HUGH KENNEDY

poetry goes far beyond eulogistic ritual, and delves profoundly into the painful mysteries of the capacity of human beings to inflict appalling suffering on others through warfare, flying in the face of common humanity. This is the most enduring message of this enriching collection of studies.

The book's most powerful chapters are those which cross-reference the ancient to the modern and contemporary, or vice versa. There is poignant irony in the statement "The history of war begins in Iraq" (p. 39) at a time when the warfare of that unfortunate country is far from accomplished. A.R. George's chapter on Akkadian war poetry goes to the heart of the painful paradoxes of the subject: the ides of glamour and heroism juxtaposed with the hell on earth which is the more common reality of the experience. Thus in the poem analyzed here, the god Erra represents brutal all-conquering violence, while his counterpart Ishum is alive to the sufferings of the victims and the consequences of destruction. Ishum also grapples with the problem of containing war within ethical parameters. This poem of Erra and Ishum explains the evils of war as a consequence of the upsetting of the cosmic balance, so undermining both human and divine order. If the cosmic bonds are undone or split, the evils of war are unleashed. In modern parlance, one might describe this as the breakdown of a coherent world order amongst our nation states.

Warfare destroys cities, along with their civilizational achievements and values. Concrete infrastructures are ruined, along with the lives of the inhabitants, and the consequent traumas may become part of recorded history. Stefan Sperl suggests, via structural analyses of convincing ingenuity, that the three poetic laments recording the destruction of Ur (c1940 BC), the destruction of Jerusalem (586 BC) and the sacking of Baghdad (AD 871) may be read as exercises in psychotherapeutic healing from the traumas of destruction, enabling the victims (and their descendants) to re-connect with themselves and their universe through the poetry. But, and this is the most powerful point Sperl makes, such healing may come at a price. In re-forging a sense of connection and identity from a collective trauma, the revived identity may be aggressive and exclusive. The "enemy" is excluded and purged from any sense of shared humanity. Hence the intractable Israeli-Palestinian conflict, which is the consequence of two collective traumas: the destruction of European Jewry and the destruction of Palestine.

Time and again throughout this volume, the ancient suffuses the modern and the contemporary like some palimpsest of horrors. Thus the poetry of al-Warraq in Hugh Kennedy's chapter details the death and destruction wrought by siege engines (*majaniq*) during the siege of Baghdad (AD 813). The *majaniq* are the ancestors of the car bombs, the mortars and the barrel bombs that are at present laying waste the peoples and the cities in the region which is the cradle of our western civilization.

The poetry of the warrior-prince Abu Firas al-Hamdani (AD 932-968), presented by Wen-chin Ouyang, is eloquent with the nostalgia felt during the period of his Byzantine captivity, but there is no evidence of the cultural exchanges such as occurred on occasion during the Crusades and the Mongol dynasties. Today in the region, such an absence of cultural encounter during captivity has been replaced by the most barbaric acts of cultural aggression. Marlé Hammond's chapter is a fascinating example of how modern colonial struggles have appropriated pre-Islamic material by adapting the poetry and the legend of Layla bt. Lukayz.

Space precludes reference to all the deserving chapters which make up a remarkable volume. A striking absence is the lack of any material from Ottoman Turkish or Persian, given the title of the book, but this is a minor complaint alongside so much that is positive. A number of the contributions combine consummate scholarship with authors' personal engagement in a theme which affects us all, some more directly than others. The poetry of this warfare is a considerable saving grace, going far beyond the limitations of eulogistic ritual, and finely illustrated in Atef Alshaer's chapter on the poetry of Mahmoud Darwish, a poetry which engages fully with "the enemy" or "the other", transcending narcissistic nationalism and embracing borderless humanity. This is the poetry of hope.

Margaret Obank reviews
Land of No Rain
by Amjad Nasser
Translated by Jonathan Wright.
BQFP, 2014.
ISBN: 978992194584. pbk, 204pp,
£12.99/$15.61.

The Nowhere Place that is home

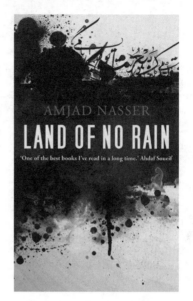

T his is Amjad Nasser's first novel, and it richly complements the Jordanian poet's many collections of poetry and travel memoirs. *Land of No Rain* is an original and unusual narrative, superbly translated by Jonathan Wright, who this year won two prizes for translation from Arabic, the Saif Ghobash Banipal Prize for Arabic Literary Translation and the Independent Foreign Fiction Prize.

The novel mirrors in many ways the author's own life as an activist, a poet and journalist who has lived and worked in the UK for many years after leaving Jordan, via periods spent in a number of other countries, as other reviewers have already documented, but it would be facile to consider that as mirroring its essence. The principal character, Adham Jaber, morphs into two selves when he returns to Hamiya, the country he fled 20 years before, where it turns out that his younger self, Younis al-Khattat, has been "waiting for ages for the opportunity that arose that night when we got talking, on the balcony of our house" to tell Adham "that it was not enough to say that things were quits". Through this dialogue Adham reflects on different periods in his life in a rare, contemplative way, his other self talking to him, worrying things out, pondering on how so much has changed irreversibly, unrecognizably. "It's all about the inner and out truth", he says.

Amjad Nasser

This form of narrative cleverly examines the role of time and place in forming an individual's character, personality and relationships, how a man such as Adham changes through age, time and space. The novel is mainly narrated by Younis, Adham's younger half, telling him, reminding him, cajoling him, facing him up to what he has been doing these 20 years away, from when he was young and very active politically to being middle-aged, conscious that everything has changed – physically, mentally, psychologically, emotionally, with no control over it. "Of course you've changed. Everyone changes, what else do you expect?" he tells himself, or rather Younis tells Adham. But that's the crux – the fact that there's realisation of change, that you're not the person you used to be and that you don't recognise the other man you were, and that other man you were doesn't recognise what you have become. In that sense the novel is a deeply philosophical questioning of one's ageing, one's memories, one's attitudes, actions and beliefs, and one's recognition of the brutality of time.

Adham Jaber was forced to flee into exile from Hamiya to the City of Red and Grey (aka London), and to take on his new name. However, an important feature of *Land of No Rain* is that, apart from the fictional Hamiya, countries and cities are not named as such, except by a description, though readers will still like to try and "identify" them. As Amjad Nasser's main concern is with investigating ageing, memory and time and their effects on character, personality and actions, getting into the detail of particular cities and countries is not part of his story. And Adham explains this by saying that he has decided to write his last book of all books, and will set his "writing free from the dates, parenthetical clauses, digressions and proper names that usually weigh it down".

Sometimes Adham doesn't quite believe he has returned, but Younis recounts to him more and more memories of how it was, the problem of his father, being punished by the disciplinary court, being caught with a banned book. Adham is trying to make sense of it all, what is true, what is not true. He had always been at loggerheads with his calligrapher father, even about the inscription over the door of their house, "Nakuja Abad", which means "nowhere place" according to the Sufi philosopher Suhrawardi, and which reminds Adham of *The City of Where*, a poetry collection by a poet from the Land of Sindbad, who can only be Sargon Boulus, the late Iraqi poet, who penned a renowned collection *Arrival in Where City*. After Younis "escaped abroad" and became Adham, he never saw his father again. He particularly quarrelled with him about the question of inner truth reflecting a higher truth, "the source of all truths". Adham is an atheist, believing that "it was people who invented the absolute, supreme and total truth, so that their final resting-place from which they could never escape, would not be in the dust. It was the need for solace, or a longing to come back again. Human narcissism. But there was no return from dust and decay. No Day of Assembly. No resurrection. No heaven and no hell." Now, back in Hamiya, Adham is seeking "peace of mind", which his young nephew helps him find through reading a complex calligraphic design of his father. He decides to take a "fresh look" at his father's works and his interest in Sahrawadi. He realizes that he became near his father when he was far, and making his own research into Sufi philosophy.

In his last discussion with Younis on the balcony Adham can finally explain things: that it is a "question of existing or not existing. In other words, of you being yourself and someone else at the same time." He can become Mr Younis and is in a position to consider mortality. He takes his young nephew Younis, named after him, and goes to visit the graves of his father and mother, but when he passes on, which of his two names will be carved there? Perhaps both?

Amjad Nasser has created an enthralling stream of consciousness novel by the unusual step of stripping back the narrative, in the main, to a philosophical dialogue in which Adham confronts his past and present through memories and ideas, something many of the author's generation are having to do in the 21st century.

Stephen Watts reviews
Nothing More to Lose
by Najwan Darwish
Translated by Kareem James Abu-Zeid
NYRB Poets, 2014,
ISBN: 9781590177303, pbk, 120pp, £7.99/$12.95

A pocketful of defiance and wit

N ajwan Darwish was born in Jerusalem in 1978, studied law in Amman and has devoted his himself to literature in the widest sense: poet, publisher, editor, organiser, advisor. He still lives in Jerusalem and published his first book of poems in 2000. He brings an enduring critical gaze to his people and home-land, to his lyric and language, to his witness and open field, and the vitiated, necessary cynicisms inherent in his sense of "nothing more to lose".

He is now hardly beyond his mid-30's (his translator is a couple of years younger) and yet it is timely that we have this book of his poetry now in English. This of course bears witness to the quality of his work, but perhaps also to the increasing prominence that the translation of contemporary Arabic poetry has attained over the past five or ten years in particular.

Think about what he says:

"But notice too how barefoot Liberty/tramples the people be-neath her" (p.19)

"My dearest friends were all Judases/they were all/men of the market" (p.29)

Or mull over the extraordinary love poem that is at one and the same time a political lament, if I am interpreting it aright: the most difficult to achieve, a love poem or a political lament that works. This is both and I'll quote in full:

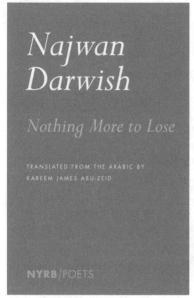

Najwan Darwish

"I rise from her love/like a man hit by a truck/I watch as
she walks away/unburdening herself/of my blood/She
really is a truck: In one go/she could wreck a hundred
men/I'm amazed at my daring/at how I died and rose
again/with so calm a heart /And here I am still at
it/heedlessly/jumping in front of another" (p.48)

The lyric certainty, exact language and groundedness of these
thirteen short lines are stunning.

Nothing More to Lose is a slight book – a hundred pages of poetry
plus a few of notes – that fits easily into the pocket. A few words of
review can hardly do it justice (a term anyway edged on the ironies
of fictional truth for the poet). It is, I'm tempted to say, a magnificent book, except that the word "magnificent" does not lie happily
with Darwish's ethics, or poetics either, so I'll just say that it is a
fine achievement, both of writing and translation.

One more thing: it is so good to see the translator thanking and
naming fellow translators (English, French and Spanish) of the
poet's work. Nothing of ownership (as there is little of that in the
poet): more of warm inclusion, of struggle and the melt of defiance
with wit, of lucidity that facilitates the shedding of limits, of
achievement discounting boundaries.

Norbert Hirschhorn reviews
Willow Trees Don't Weep
by **Fadia Faqir**
Heron Books, UK, 2014.
ISBN 978-1782069508. Pbk, 288pp,
£7.99/$6.30, Kindle £3.96/$6.74.

A story of forgiveness

In 1986 Amman, Najwa was three years old when her father Omar Rahman, a nurse, abandoned his family. Omar had dreams, he was a "man who wanted to walk around the world". Unable to indulge his neurotic, weepy wife he took instead to Amman nightlife in the company of his childhood friend Hani. Impotent after an alcohol-fueled night, Hani joins an Islamic study circle to purify himself and becomes a fundamentalist seeking to restore the Caliphate. Omar is pious, but hardly extreme. Nonetheless, when Hani decides to join the jihad against Soviet forces in Afghanistan, Omar's loyalty to his friend, the opportunity to join in a great adventure, and the prospect of freedom from his wife, compel him to go along. He will miss Najwa most of all. In fury, his wife turns bitterly secularist, forbidding any token or practice of Islam, either in the house or by her daughter.

Beginning in 2010, Najwa tells her story in the first person. Her mother has died a horrible death from stomach cancer and her grandmother now insists that Najwa should go and find her father because: "I'll not last long. You cannot live in this house on your own after I'm gone. What would people say? Only loose women live alone. You belong with your father."

Based on this thin premise (other possibilities to protect reputation surely existed), the author sends her protagonist on a dangerous journey to Pakistan, Afghanistan, and finally to England to find her father. Najwa is often wilful, hysterical, full of hatred for both parents, often taking it out physically on herself, yet unable to cry. She is also needy for the kind of attention her father once gave, making her vulnerable to another form of abandonment when a man offers

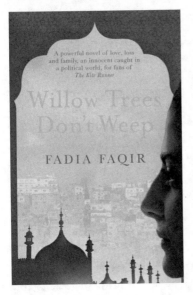

Photo: Philip Ryott

Fadia Faqir

kindness. Only the various women she encounters along the way nurture her as her grandmother did.

Najwa is passed along a chain of jihadists until she finds herself in a large compound in Afghanistan, a training base for al-Qaida troops. She discovers that her father is revered for his courage and his surgical prowess, providing life-saving amputations for injured fighters. He has, however, taken a second wife, fathering Najwa's half-sister Amani, whom Najwa jealously despises. It is only when a drone strike on the compound kills Amani that the first hints of forgiveness enter her mind.

Omar Rahman, disgusted by the slaughter of Muslims by western forces, had become a global jihadist and had been sent to England where he recruited and trained four young British Muslims, who blew up buses and underground trains in July 2005. He has been imprisoned for life in Durham high security prison.

The book's trajectory is established through Najwa's story, interspersed with Omar's diary entries from January 1986 – in the run-up to his absconding from Amman – to June 2011, with the two narratives coming together in the denouement. Although I found the diary entries authorial, in ways that often force twists in the plot, nevertheless, one keeps turning the pages to enjoy the adept storyteller's technique – "and then . . . and then . . . "

Susannah Tarbush reviews

Rain over Baghdad
by Hala El Badry

translated by Farouk Abdel Wahab
The American University in Cairo Press, 2014
ISBN 978 977 416 588 7. Pbk, 512 pp,
£11.97/$19.95. Kindle £8.74/$14.06

Three knocks on the door

This structurally and thematically ambitious novel is set between Iraq and Egypt in the 1970s and 1980s, a time when
many Egyptians went to work in Iraq. The Egyptian first-
person narrator Noura moves to Baghdad as a bride in 1975 to join
her engineer husband Hatim. She finds works as a journalist in the
Baghdad bureau of an Egyptian magazine under the directorship of
a veteran Egyptian communist, Hilmi Amin. Her colleagues include
Anhar Khayun, a woman from the marshes of southern Iraq who in
1979 vanishes without trace.

Noura and Hatim return to live in Egypt after the Iran-Iraq war
erupts in September 1980. A year and a half later Noura is invited
back to Baghdad for a conference on the education of newly-literate

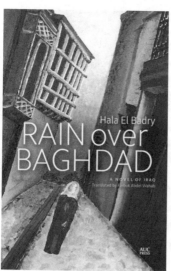

women. During this visit she tries
to find out what lay behind
Anhar's disappearance, and to un-
cover the truth of Anhar's relationship with Hilmi. At the same
time she is carrying a letter to a
young Egyptian man from his family, begging him to leave the Iraq
army and come home to Egypt.

Rain over Baghdad is a demanding but highly rewarding read. It
has an intricate structure, cycling
through time and space. Gradually, patterns emerge and secrets
are laid bare. The narrative several

times returns to Noura's visit to Baghdad, with the repetition of a paragraph beginning: "Three knocks on the door of memory restored life to days that were lingering as they turned towards disappearing forever. I tugged at the end of the thread of time that used to tame mountains and humans. The days broke loose and came tumbling down on my heart."

El Badry gives a chilling portrait of Iraq under the bloody rise of the power of Saddam Hussein. At the same time various characters are caught up in the turmoil triggered in Egypt by President Sadat's signing of the Camp David Accords with Israel and the crackdown on his opponents.

Hala El Badry

The author explores the emotions of her characters with sensitivity, writing erotic scenes with frankness and sensuality. While two of the characters have a passionate but tortured love affair, as revealed in their private writings, Noura and Hatim enjoy a happy, sexually fulfilling marriage. But Noura suffers over the separation from her young sons while she is away from Egypt. A recurring motif is the leaking of milk from her breasts as she longs for the suckling infant she has left behind.

El Badry is both a prizewinning novelist and deputy editor-in-chief of Egypt's radio and television magazine. *Rain Over Bahgdad* is the third of her novels to be published by AUC Press in English translation, after *A Certain Woman* (2003, also translated by Farouk Abdel Wahab) and *Muntaha* (2006, translated by Nancy Roberts).

Rain Over Baghdad is the last published translation by Farouk Abdel Wahab, the pen name of the Egyptian scholar and translator Farouk Abdel Wahab Mustafa who died on 3 April 2013. He was Ibn Rushd Professorial Lecturer in Modern Arabic Language in the Department of Near Eastern Languages and Civilizations, and Associate Director of the Center for Middle Eastern Studies, both at the University of Chicago. Abdel Wahab translated numerous Arabic works of fiction, and won the 2007 Saif Ghobash Banipal Prize for Arabic Literary Translation for *The Lodging House* by fellow Egyptian Khairy Shalaby (AUC Press 2006).

Peter Clark reviews
The Bridges of Constantine
by **Ahlem Mosteghanemi**
translated by Raphael Cohen
Bloomsbury Publishing, UK, 2013.
ISBN: 978-1408846407. Hbk, 320 pp,
£16.99/$19.99. Kindle £12.85/$13.13.

A new title
and new translation

This book has had a singular gestation. The Algerian Ahlam Mostaghanemi's prize-winning novel was first published as *Dhakirat al-Jasad* in Beirut in 1993. It achieved an immediate success, and was read widely throughout the Arab world. It clearly resonated with the generation that were the children of the pioneers of Arab independence in general and of Algerian in particular.

A translation into English by Baria Ahmar Srei was published by the American University in Cairo Press in 2000 with the title *Memory in the Flesh*, same as the Arabic. I reviewed this translation for the seventh issue of *Banipal* in 2000. I praised the book but pointed out defects in the translation, which did a disservice to the original. I argued that there was a need to revise meticulously the Arabic original and the English rendering and expressed the hope that AUC Press could arrange this before the next printing. I was then asked by AUC Press to undertake these tasks myself, which I duly did. My revised translation came out in 2003 and was distributed in the United Kingdom by Arabia Books in 2008.

We now have a new edition, a new translation, by Raphael Cohen, which improves on my revision. It has a new title, and the author's name has a new English spelling. Bloomsbury has been able to mobilise its resources and expertise in marketing and promotion, and the new book has been reviewed by, among other organs, *The Times* and the *Daily Mail*. Raphael Cohen's very good translation corrects some faults I made, including errors that I had charged Bahia Ahmar Sreih of being guilty. The whole production of the book is excellent.

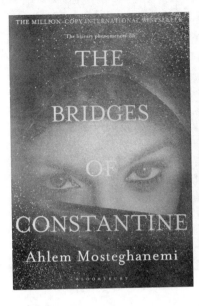

Ahlem Mosteghanemi

The change in the title is instructive. The earlier title, like the original Arabic, implied the psychological aspects of the story. The newer title brings out the significance of the city of Constantine, which meant so much to the principal characters in the novel. The bridges implicitly reflect the bridges of Paris over which the protagonist Khaled's studio looked.

Ahlem Mosteghanemi's novel is the anguished statement of a generation but nonetheless stands the test of time. It is experimental with a kind of second person narrative. It focuses on Khaled, a veteran of the Algerian independence campaign, a one-armed painter in Paris who meets the daughter of an old comrade. He knew her when she was an infant. The relationship is deftly drawn with a background of disillusion with the corruption and consumerism of the new leaders of the country. These were characterised by "pretence and extreme hypocrisy, the telltale signs of newly and rapidly acquired wealth and status. . . . [They] specialised in public slogans and secret deals." The Sreih/Clark version expressed this: ". . . a meretriciousness in their newly acquired wealth and their latest fashions . . . [They were] experts in saying the right thing and wheeling and dealing."

In third century BC, Alexandria Ptolemy summoned seventy-two scholars to translate the Torah from Hebrew to Greek. The scholars were housed in separate quarters without having access to one another. In due time they emerged with their translations and it turned out – miraculously – that each version was identical. It is clear from these samples that Ahlem Mosteghanemi's novel has not undergone the same fate. Indeed comparison of the three English versions would be a useful exercise in translation studies.

Not even Naguib Mahfouz has had three translations of any of his novels. When an authoritative text – by Homer, Dante or Cervantes or *A Thousand and One Nights* – is subject to multiple translations each successive version often reflects the generation and cultural world of the translator. But three translations in just fifteen years is remarkable. Will we be due for a fourth in 2020?

Susannah Tarbush reviews
Days of Ignorance
by Laila Aljohani
translated by Nancy Roberts
BQFP, July 2014. ISBN 978-9992195192. Hbk, 165 pp, £9.99/$15.13.
Kindle £7.73/$12/44

A gripping family drama

Days of Ignorance by Laila Aljohani is a family drama that reveals much about Saudi society. Its central character Leen is a 30-year-old unmarried Saudi graduate. For some years she has been involved in a clandestine relationship with Malek, a black man who grew up in Saudi Arabia but has so far been denied citizenship. Racism is a main theme of the compactly-written novel; the glossary includes such derogatory terms for black people as "takruni", "kur", and "kuwayha".

Leen's brother Hashem, a pampered womanising layabout ten years her junior, is disgusted by Leen's love for Malek whom he thinks of as "the animal". He and a friend beat Malek so brutally that he is left lying in a coma in hospital. Hashem is distraught at the possibility that Malek will die. He reflects on his meaningless

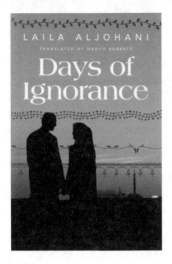

Laila Aljohani

life compared with that of his sister with her job and love of books.

The novel is set in the holy city of Madinah in "the twelfth year after Desert Storm", the 1991 war that defeated Iraq after its invasion of Kuwait. The ominous backdrop is the buildup to a new war, the 2003 US-led invasion of Iraq. Each chapter is dated, the names of the months being those used in the pre-Islamic days of "jahiliya", meaning "ignorance". In successive chapters the gripping narrative switches between the streams of consciousness of Leen, Hashem, Malek and Leen's father. The liberal-minded father is sympathetic to Leen, but has refused permission to allow Malek to marry her because he thinks society would never accept her marriage to a black man. Leen's mother, who has always idolised and spoilt her son, rages at Leen and blames her for Hashem's attack on Malek. The pressures on Leen rise to a crescendo as the airstrikes on Iraq begin.

Laila Aljohani is an award-winning Saudi writer born in Tabuk in 1969. *Days of Ignorance*, translated by Nancy Roberts, is her first novel to be published in English translation. A chapter of the novel, translated by Piers Amodia under the title *Jahiliya*, appeared in *Banipal 34*. Amodia's translation of an excerpt from the novel *The Waste Paradise* by Aljohani (al-Juhni), was published in *Banipal 20*.

Follow us on twitter @BanipalMagazine
https://www.twitter.com/BanipalMagazine

FICTION

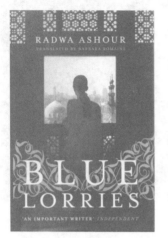

Blue Lorries by Radwa Ashour is the latest novel by this important Egyptian writer to be translated into English. Writing with a penetrating clarity, Ashour writes of a political storm in a way that is remarkably calm and measured. The protagonist of *Blue Lorries*, Nada Abdel Qadir, never quite manages to grow out of the temper-tantrums that characterize her childhood and adolescence. Nor does she ever manage to shake her almost obsessive observation of omens. Her interest in politics develops early in life – after a summer spent in Paris in the immediate aftermath of the 1968 student-led protests.

The trip is an eye-opener on many levels. Her fascination with prison life, however, stems even earlier, after her father is absent from much of her childhood as a political prisoner. Nada's ambitious project – to compile a book about life in prisons across time and space – is sparked by her lifelong fascination by prison life and the pursuit of freedom. Nada's story interlocks with those of other Egyptian political activists and their painful stories. Ashour's novel *Spectres*, also translated by Barbara Romaine, was runner-up in the 2011 Saif Ghobash Banipal Prize for Arabic Literary Translation. Published by Bloomsbury Qatar Foundation Publishing, ISBN: 9789992194485. Hbk, 239pp, £12.99/$17.93 Kindle £6.69/$10.76. Clare Roberts

The Woman from Tantoura by Radwa Ashour asks many pertinent questions about Palestine's history. Ruqayya is a young girl from the Palestinian village of Tantoura, south of Haifa, when violent attacks on her village and the massacre of many of her family members force her and her mother to flee. The 1948 Nakba signals her introduction to the traumatic life of a refugee. This book brings up the stories of many who, like Ruqayya, lost their dreams, homes and family members in the Nakba. She is forced to move from Tantoura to Sidon in south Lebanon, then to Beirut, witnessing at first hand the difficulties of holding refugee status, the pain

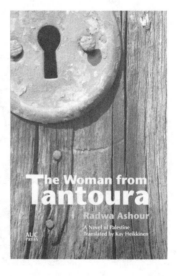

of separation from home and loved ones and near impossibility of relinquishing any hope of return, and the horrors of massacres and civil war. It is a story of Ruqayya's own life and that of her family and relatives, and the equally painful stories of those she encounters in the camps and elsewhere. Translated by Kay Heikkinen. AUC Press, 2014. ISBN: 9789774166150. Pbk, 356 pp, £10.40/$15.90. CR.

Maps of the Soul by Ahmed Fagih contains the first three translated volumes of the novelist's 12-volume historical novel of the same name. It is the story of Othman al-Sheikh, who is forced to leave his village in the Libyan desert for 1930s Tripoli in order to escape his past. The volumes describe his encounters in this city, still under Italian occupation. All three volumes, *Bread of the City*, *Sinful Pleasures* and *Naked Runs the Soul*, make striking use of the second person. Other writing by Fagih is included in *Banipal* 3, and 4 and the special issue on Libyan Fiction, *Banipal 40*. Translated by Thorayya Allam and Brian Loo. Published by Darf Publishers, ISBN: 978-1-85077-271-2. Pbk, 612pp, £10.99/$12.93 Kindle $8.11. CR

Butterfly Wings by Mohamed Salmawy has been heralded as the novel that predicted the 2011 Egyptian Revolution. Trapped and frustrated by her passionless marriage to a senior government figure, fashion designer Doha struggles to find freedom even when she leaves Egypt. But when she meets leading dissident and academic Dr Ashraf al-Zayni on a plane journey to Italy, she is forced to reconsider her entire perspective on life, love and politics.

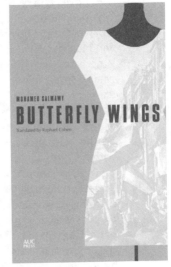

As anti-government demonstrations spread across Egypt, and with the help of Dr Ashraf, Doha's realization that politics is personal causes her whole world to change. The stories of Doha and Ashraf interweave with that of Ayman, who is on his own quest to find his real mother. Butterfly imagery pervades the novel, from the patterns on Doha's fashion designs to the personal and national pursuit of freedom. Translated by Raphael Cohen, AUC Press, 2014. ISBN: 9789774166426. Pbk, 144 pages, £10.99/$13.19. CR

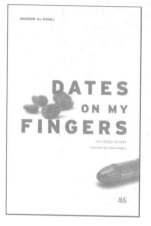

Dates on my Fingers by Muhsin Al-Ramli is a darkly intriguing story. When Saleem's sister is groped by the son of an important Iraqi official, their father Noah takes his revenge by forcing a bullet up the anus of the perpetrator. This moment of rage results in years of suffering for Noah and his wider family, a conservative tribe who shun modern society and all things related to the Iraqi regime. Centred around the most revered Grandfather Mutlaq, the clan tries to live in isolation from all that it resents.

Saleem's father Noah encapsulates the most conservative and honour-driven aspects of their way of thinking. So, when Saleem, years later in his self-imposed exile from Iraq, stumbles across his father groping a girl in a Madrid nightclub, he struggles to reconcile his father's conflicting identities. So, too, does he struggle to forget his passion for his cousin Aliya, who had tragically drowned in the nearby river years earlier. Stumbling across his radically changed father brings back bittersweet memories and raises new questions about exile, identity, sexuality, family and revenge. Translated by Luke Leafgren, AUC Press, April/June 2014. ISBN: 9789774166440. Pbk, 192pp, £8.52/$3.73, Kindle £7.71/$12.40. CR

The novel **Diary of a Jewish Muslim** by Egyptian author Kamal Ruhayyim tells the story of Galal, a boy born to a Jewish mother and Muslim father in 1930s Cairo. The story is narrated delightfully by Galal himself, beginning in his infancy, as his mother's family learn of his father's death fighting in the Egyptian army. The story unfolds as Galal grows up, grappling with school and teenage crushes, yet also with his complex identity within Egypt.

His is an honest, vivid and often amusing voice, and his daily life demonstrates the increasingly tense experience of Jewish Egyptians, as well as the closely-knit social fabric of old Cairo in the 1940s and 50s. The reader sees this rising anxiety in his attempts to forge his own identity, despite having been raised effectively in neither religion. At school and by his father's family he is regarded as Jewish, and yet comes to identify as Muslim, attending prayers during Ramadan and even unwisely asking a sheikh to convert his mother. Galal is extremely close to his mother and grandfather, to whom the issue of emigration becomes ever more pertinent with the image of his grandfather's old tarboosh left behind being particularly poignant. Ruhayyim's previous novel, *Days in the Diaspora* (reviewed in *Banipal 46*) follows the life of Galal and his family in Paris. Fluidly translated by Sarah Enany, who also translated *Days in the Diaspora*, this novel is a charming, touching story of a boy's ever more complicated quest for identity. AUC Press, May 2014. ISBN: 9789774166433. Pbk, 224pp. £12.99/$16.39. Zoe Dexter

Ishmael's Oranges by Claire Hajaj has at its heart the marriage between a Palestinian Arab refugee, originally from Jaffa, and a British Jewish woman whose grandparents fled pogroms in Russia. Salim and Jude fall in love as students in swinging 1960s London and marry, despite opposition from their families. But this novel is no uplifting "love shall conquer all" story. Over time the differences between the two become ever more pronounced, particularly after they go to live in Kuwait. The couple's girl and boy twins, and especially the sensitive artistic boy, carry the burden of their parents' conflict against a background of repeated Middle East wars and traumas.

This is the first novel by Hajaj, who is herself the daughter of a Palestinian-Jewish marriage. She switches between the viewpoints of Salim and Jude, from their childhoods up to the late 1980s. Hajaj successfully sustains the momentum from the mysterious prologue to the dramatic final climax, although some readers may be uncomfortable with certain details of the Palestinian and Jewish perspectives. Oneworld Publications, UK. July 2014. ISBN: 978-1780744940. Hbk, 336pp, £13.59 /$17.48. Pbk £8.99. Kindle £8.54/$16.40. Susannah Tarbush

POETRY

Love Letters in the Sand: The Love Poems of Khalil Gibran is simply an exquisite little book. First published in 2005, this is the first collection in English of Gibran's writings on love in all its guises. In Gibran's famously lyrical, mystical style, these poems tell the course of love through the seasons, beautifully interpreted by Tunisian calligrapher Lassaâd Metoui, whose calligraphy adorns each page of this collection.

Souvenir Press, London, 2014 (latest edition). 96pp, hbk, £9.99/$10.19. ZD

Diaspo/Renga: A collaboration in alternating Renga, created by poets Marilyn Hacker and Deema K Shehabi, is a lyrical poetic conversation, a renga of a new style to the traditional age-old Japanese form. It was created between 2009 and 2013 after Marilyn Hacker, in Paris, sent a single poem to Deema Shehabi, in California, following the Gaza war of 2009. As the publisher says, it is "a dignified celebration of humanity in and among atrocities". In lines sprinkled with Arabic (transliterated in French format) the poets range across continents, emotions and experiences, across Syrian, Iraqi and Palestinian landscapes of loss, of war, of tents and refugees. The poets link hearts and words across history and metaphors, as well as empty streets, razed villages and cold winds, bringing to readers a great cast of characters whose voices clamour to be heard. A very successful poetic experiment, though more careful copy-editing would have caught a number of spelling mistakes in both the English and the transliterated Arabic. Published by Holland Park Press, 2014. ISBN: 9781907320422. Pbk. 126pp, £8.99/$15.20. Margaret Obank

A collaboration in alternating Renga by
Marilyn Hacker and Deema K Shehabi

Diaspo/Renga

MEMOIR

A Muslim on the Bridge: On Being an Iraqi-Arab in the Twenty-First Century by Iraqi architect and artist Ali Shakir is a highly personal exploration of his thoughts and experiences as a self-proclaimed liberal Iraqi-Arab Muslim. He articulates on a vast array of issues, such as Saddam's rise to power, polygamy, poverty, patriarchal systems, terrorism, and the dying art of coffee-making, to name but a few. Intertwined within these topics is his reflection on the role of Islam in Arab societies (each chapter begins with a passage from the Qur'an, which he then critically considers) and his own Islam and life experiences – namely, as the son of a Shia father and Sunni mother, raised in the largely secular middle-class world of 1970s and 80s Baghdad.

The book takes the form of intimate musings, arranged in series of ostensibly unconnected

"scenes". Shakir is honest and personal throughout, explaining the confusion he has experienced whilst negotiating his own relationship with Islam, Iraq, and the world at large, in a diary format both enjoyable and touching to read. Though an intimate exploration of one person's grappling with many issues and their intersections in daily life, religion, society, and contemporary history, this articulate investigation will likely resonate much further. Signal 8 Press, 2013. ISBN 978-988-15542-9-1. 296pp, £10.70/$15.26. Kindle £5.14/$8.52. Nook $7.99. ZD

NON-FICTION

A Sleepless Eye: Aphorisms by Tuareg writer Ibrahim al-Koni is a carefully selected collection of stunning aphorisms, translated from the Arabic by Roger Allen. Despite having gained increasing international attention in recent years for his novels and stories, it is al-Koni's aphorisms that now take centre stage. Based around the themes of nature, the seasons, desert, water, sea, wind, rock, trees and flowers, and fire, the aphorisms are profound words of wisdom, which reflect al-Koni's own spiritual relationship with the Libyan desert.

By devoting many of the aphorisms to man's relationship with nature, the work also presses readers to take in their natural surroundings, and, more importantly, to respect and preserve them. After reading this presentation of the natural world, readers cannot help but feel more intimately linked to it. The symbiotic relationship between the different elements is also explored, along with the timelessness of rock, the fleetingness of flowers in bloom, and the freedom found at the depths of the sea, a freedom we long for yet fear. Al-Koni's work is a lyrical homage to all that is important yet often overlooked in today's world. Beautiful photos of the desert (mostly by Alain Sèbe) aid our meditation as we ponder al-Koni's powerful words. Selected by Hartmut Fähndrich, translated by Roger Allen, Syracuse University Press, 2014. ISBN: 9780815610342. Hbk, 118pp. £12.55/$13.17. CR

Contemporary Arab-American Literature: Transnational Reconfigurations of Citizenship and Belonging by Carol Fadda-Conrey is a comparative study addressing the transgression of Arab-American identities in fiction, essays and memoirs, including a few examples of film and arts. Originally a dissertation, the material ranges from the 1990s onwards, including a separate chapter dedicated to the representations of Arabs and Muslims after 9/11. While wars and conflicts in the Middle East have given rise to negative perceptions of Arab identities and cultures in USA, the interest for literature by Arab-American authors has increased. The authors are, however, still working in a context where Arabs are stereotyped as harem girls and terrorist villains, and their American citizenship and belonging is constantly questioned. Articulating a transformed self-representation, Fadda-Conrey shows how Arab-American authors are instead trying to

capture the complexity and heterogeneity of their communities.

The chapters show a wide range of approaches from the representations of Arab homelands and the experience of returning to ancestral homelands, to Arab-American transnational identities and a new understanding of what it entails being an American. Analysing works such as Lawrence Joseph's poem "Sand Nigger", William Blatty's autobiography *Which Way to Mecca, Jack?*, Samia Serageldin's novel *The Cairo House* and Annemarie Jacir's film "Salt of this Sea", Fadda-Conrey concludes that works such as these broaden and alter the rigid parameters of national identities and their belonging to the US society. American Literatures Initiative Series, NYU Press, USA/UK. 2014. ISBN: 9781479804313. Pbk, 272pp, illustrated, £14.60/$21.85. Kindle £12.52.

Aurora Tellenbach

Libya's Hidden Pages of History: A Memoir by Mustafa Ben-Halim is a personal and political account of Libya in the 1950s, by one of that decade's most prominent politicians and prime ministers. From Libyan independence in 1951 and the fall of the Saqizli government to the rise of the Senussi movement and discovery of oil, the Algerian Revolution, the Tripartite Aggression and ties with Egyptian leader Gamal Abdel Nasser, this book is a comprehensive account of Libya in its early years of independence. The work describes Libya's relationship with its neighbours, the rise of Arab nationalism, and Libya's clashes with the British and French during a most formative decade. It sets Libyan history in its wider Middle Eastern and international context, and provides a multitude of newly-released documents and telegrams. As an autobiography of a senior politician it is highly readable and accessible; full of sensitive and astute observations and entertaining anecdotes. Translated by Leslie McLoughlin. Published by Rimal Publications, Cyprus, 2014. ISBN: 978 9963 610 75 4. Pbk, 544pp, £18.99/$20. CR

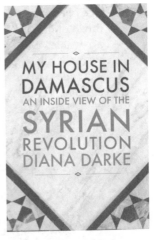

My House in Damascus by Diana Darke differs from other works to have emerged from the conflict currently raging in Syria. Having made the radical decision in 2005 to purchase a traditional courtyard house in the historic old city of Damascus, Diana Darke, author of the Bradt guide to Syria, gave everything she had to restoring it. Now acting as a shelter and home for dozens of displaced Syrians in the Civil War, the house has taken on a new role. Full of historical detail, this personal and painful book is a tribute to Damascus and all that draws people, locals and foreigners alike, to it. Simultaneously heart breaking and uplifting, it is an important and unique read for those wishing to gain more understanding of the situation in Syria, and will strike many a chord with those for whom it already holds special significance. The book is full of humorous anecdotes, such as those about the frustrating pace of Syrian bureaucracy, and beautiful descriptions, such as that of the courtyard house itself. Haus Publishing. ISBN: 978-1-908323-64-4. Hbk, 254pp, £14.99/ $18.42. CR

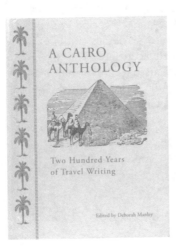

A Cairo Anthology: Two Hundred Years of Travel Writing, edited by Deborah Manley, is a charmingly presented survey of Cairo in the eyes of those who have visited it over the centuries. Extracts included range in tone and style, from the writings of Lord Byron, Sir Richard Burton and Sophia Poole to Murray's Handbook for Travellers in Egypt and Florence Nightingale's Letters from Egypt. All cast their own light on this timeless city. AUC Press, 2013. ISBN: 978-977-416-612-9. Hbk, 150pp, £11.68/$18.95. CR

Women Travelers in Egypt: From the Eighteenth to the Twenty-First Century edited by Deborah Manley, is much in the same vein as its shorter counterpart, but entirely composed of writings and observations by the fairer sex. The anecdotes detail journeys of women in Cairo, Luxor and along the Nile and the Sinai, shedding light on a range of delicate matters, from the least disagreeable way to ascend the Pyramids (namely, allowing three Arabs to lift each woman) to the art of arranging mosquito curtains. AUC Press. ISBN: 9789774165702. Pbk, 216pp, £12.99/$22.95 CR

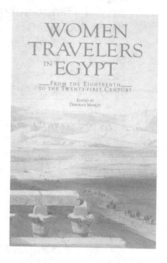

Authentic Egyptian Cooking: From the Table of Abou El Sid by Nehal Lehata is a tribute to Egypt's best loved dishes. Abou El Sid, one of Cairo's most popular restaurants, prizes itself on its delicious home-food and hospitality, and this book is testament to such qualities. Full-page photos accompany all 57 dishes. The recipes are fuss-free and unintimidating, relishing in simplicity and special personal touches, including favourites such as koshari, Om Ali, taameya, fettah and molokheya. Each recipe contains insightful cultural details and introduces those unacquainted with Egyptian life to some of the country's best loved customs and traditions. A beautiful tribute to Egyptian food. AUC Press, 2014. ISBN: 9789774166211. Hbk, 144pp, $18.99/$2995. CR

AOE TANAMI

A Dialogue with
Arab Literature
in Osaka and Tokyo

Autumn is the best season in Japan for arts and literature. This year was no exception despite the exceptionally powerful typhoons and the volcanic eruption that caught the archipelago by surprise. On 14th October in Osaka University and 19th in Seikei University in west Tokyo, symposia entitled "Expression, Identity and Crossing Borders: A Dialogue with Arab Literature" were held with three visiting Arab authors – the Iraqi author and Banipal editor Samuel Shimon, the celebrated Lebanese-born author Rawi Hage from Canada, and the young Egyptian author Mona Prince. The events were inspired by the Asia Africa Latin America Literature Forum that has taken place annually in South Korea since 2010, and by the activities of Banipal over the

Rawi Hage, Mona Prince and Samuel Shimon in Osaka University, photo by Tomoko Fukuda

Lee Chonghwa, Director for Asian and Pacific Studies, Professor, Faculty of Law

Yoichi Kamejima, President of Seikei University

years to broaden the readers of modern Arab literature around the world and encourage Arab writers and literary translators. It was not only as a co-ordinator of the symposia and a researcher in Middle East Studies, but also as a lover of literature that I enthusiastically embraced this opportunity to introduce modern Arab literature to the current Japanese book market, which seems hesitant to accept non-western literature, and espe-

cially Arab literature.

In Osaka (the day after the Typhoon Vongfong passed through), most of our audience were students studying Arabic and/or interested in the Arab world. Samuel Shimon fascinated the younger audience by talking about his dramatic life history, and introducing his work on Banipal magazine. Beginning with a reading from her novel *'inni uhaddithka li-tara* (*So You May See*), Mona Prince talked about

Aoe Tanami, interpreter Mori Shintaro and Mohammad Khashan

Samuel Shimon and Mona Prince in Seikei University,

her personal relation with writing and her experience during the January 2011 Revolution in Egypt. Rawi Hage spoke about his three novels, his life as a child during the Lebanese Civil War, and later in USA and Canada as an immigrant, discussing the significance of writing fiction at all points as an individual and as an atheist.

With a sense of achievement, we left Osaka and travelled on to Tokyo, my home base. Here I want to add that these symposia were organized as part of a larger project, "Mahrajan (Festival) 2014", which included other events with Mona Prince and Rawi Hage as well as with Mohammed Khashan from Palestine/Lebanon, who discussed his memoir – excerpted in *Banipal 46* – plus a Palestine Poster Exhibition. "Mahrajan 2014" was made possible by the

co-operation of local citizens, especially the residents of Koenji, an area of Tokyo.

After a special session on Mohammed Khashan's oral history the previous day, the symposium at Seikei University had a wide-ranging audience of researchers, editors, publishers and the reading public. After opening with an address by the university president Yoichi Kamejima, and by the director of the Center for Asian Pacific Studies, Lee Chonghwa, I spoke of my hopes and expectations for the symposium and its aftermath. The lineup of the guests itself, I added, suggested the varieties of contemporary Arab literature that existed for Japanese readers, who generally had a limited image of it.

Samuel Shimon's opening speech created a passionate atmosphere for the whole event.

Masakuni Ota and Masatsugu Ono

His introduction, which focused on his personal experience of reading Yusuf Idris and Naguib Mahfouz, and especially Taha Hussein, led the audience into this world of modern classics of Arab literature. After referring to his hardships after leaving Iraq, his meeting Arab writers in Paris, he read aloud of a few lines from his autobiographical novel *Iraqi fi Paris* (*An Iraqi in Paris*). Then he explained how the founding of Banipal magazine started a new epoch in the scene of contemporary Arab literature.

Mona Prince opened with the statement that it was difficult to be a liberal woman in Egypt. Looking back at her rebellious childhood, and to the growth of

Rawi Hage and Hidemitsu Kuroki at Tokyo University of Foreign Studies

l to r: Interpreters were Professors Tetsuya Motohashi, Midori Hiraga, Yoshiaki Fukuda, Caitlin Stronell

Kaoru Yamamoto

Kaoru Yamamoto's article on "Arabic Literature in Japan" will be published in Banipal 52

the Islamic movement in Egypt through many Egyptians returning from working in Saudi Arabia, she explained how she had broken one of Egypt's taboos, namely sex, in writing a novel that criticized male domination in a sexual relationship. The reading she had selected from her novel supported this.

Focusing on the word "Identity" from the symposium's title, Rawi Hage spoke about Arab identity: it is historically multicultural and as such contains minorities, and it exists as a result of compromise and the mix of many religions and cultures. In his first novel *De Niro's Game*, which is an existential novel and a reaction to the religious aspect of the Lebanese Civil war, he described the aspiration for reconciliation among the people of Lebanon even though reality did not allow it. Then, introducing his second novel *Cockroach*, he suggested that the very act of narration released a person from his/her personal tragedy and formed the historical story that would then allow the reader to consider the manner of questioning itself.

The Seikei symposium included three prominent Japanese guest commentators. First, Kaoru Yamamoto, a specialist of Arabic literature, spoke about Arabic literature and its Japanese readers and recent efforts by Japanese researchers to introduce it more widely. Masakuni Ota, who has long experience as an editor, described the significance of cultural exchange between writers, looking back his experience of the Asian-African Writers' Conference. Masatsugu Ono, a writer and a scholar of French literature, praised Samuel Shimon's autobiographical novel in the highest terms, having read it in French translation, and recommended its translation into Japanese.

The over five hours of this rich and rewarding symposium flew past, and was filled throughout with excitement. I felt a profound joy at being a reader of Arab literature and being able to share my love for it with all the participants.

Oki Kiyota, Editor-in-Chief of Subaru, the well-known Japanese literary magazine, with two colleagues Fukiku Kanaseki (l) and Chieko Kawasaki (r) following a meeting with Banipal's editor Samuel Shimon to plan future collaboration between the two magazines on publishing Arab authors in Japanese translation.

CELEBRATING SAADI YOUSSEF –
AUTHORS AND TRANSLATORS

Salih Altoma was born in Iraq. He is Professor Emeritus of Arabic and Comparative Literature at Indiana University, USA, and has been associated with the university since 1964. He has published works in Arabic and English on modern Arabic literature, and on Arab and Western literary relations, including *Modern Arabic Literature in Translation: A Companion* (Saqi, 2006), and *The Yearbook of Comparative and General Literature* (guest editor, 2000) on the theme of Arab-Western Literary Relations.

Mona Anis is a writer and translator from Egypt. She is presently Senior Editorial Consultant with Dar al-Shorouk, a leading Arab publisher. She was a Culture Editor and Deputy Editor-in-Chief of *Al-Ahram Weekly*. Her translations into English include poetry by Mahmoud Darwish, Saadi Youssef, Ahmed Fouad Negm and Abdel Rahman El-Abnoudi.

Salah Awwad is an Iraqi poet and journalist, born in 1956 in Bagdad. He left Iraq in 1979 and in 1988 settled in the USA. He has two poetry collections and his work is published in several anthologies. He works as a journalist at the UN in New York.

Hussein bin Hamza was born in Al-Hassaka, Syria, in 1963. Since 1995 he has lived and worked in Beirut as a journalist on cultural affairs for several newspapers there, such as *An-Nahar, As-Safir, Al-Balad*. He now works for *Al-Akhbar*. He has two collections of poetry with selected poems published in *Banipal 33*.

Camillo Gómez-Rivas is currently an Assistant Professor of Mediterranean Studies at the University of California, Santa Cruz, after teaching Middle Eastern History at the AUC for several years. He is a Banipal contributing editor.

Rawi Hage is a Lebanese novelist, based in Canada, the author of three best-selling novels, *Carnival* (2012), *Cockroach* (2008) and *De Niro's Game* (2006). Each was awarded the Hugh MacLennan Prize for Fiction, with *De Niro's game* also winning the international IMPAC prize and the McAuslan First Book Prize.

Jack Hirschman is a prolific American poet, painter, translator and social activist. In 2006 he was appointed Poet Laureate of San Francisco and in 2007 he was the key organiser of the first San Francisco International Poetry Festival, now biennale. In partnership with Friends of the San Francisco Public Library and the San Francisco Public Library, he has also presented smaller poetry festivals in a variety of languages, including the Latino Poetry Festival, the Vietnamese Poetry Festival and the Iranian Arts Poetry Festival. He is active with the Revolutionary Poets

Brigade and curates the *Poets 11* Anthology.

Yair Huri is a senior lecturer of Arabic literature and the director of the Program of Arabic language and Literature at Ben Gurion University of the Negev, Israel. He has also been a visiting lecturer at New York University and Skidmore College.

William Maynard Hutchins is a professor in the Philosophy & Religion Department of Appalachian State University in Boone, North Carolina, USA. He has translated many contemporary Arab authors, and was joint-winner of the 2013 Saif Ghobash Banipal Prize for his translation of *A Land Without Jasmine* by Wajdi al-Ahdal (Garnet, 2012).

Mansour Mansour is an Iraqi artist, based in Germany since 1987. He graduated from the Academy of Fine Art, Baghdad, the Academy of Art, Perugia, and University of the Arts, Berlin. He has worked as a freelance illustrator for publishing houses, advertising agencies and organisations and has held many solo exhibitions of his works in Iraq, the Netherlands, Germany, UK, Denmark, Tunisia, Algeria, Armenia and Georgia.

Khaled Mattawa is a Libyan American poet, the author of four collections of poetry and a major translator of contemporary Arabic poets. His Adonis: *Selected Poems* (2010) won the 2011 Saif Ghobash-Banipal Prize for Arabic Literary Translation and was shortlisted for the 2011 International Griffin Prize for Poetry. In January 2014 he became a Chancellor of the Academy of American Poets and in September he was awarded a MacArthur Fellowship.

Peter Money is an American writer and has been publishing his work since 1985. In the late 1980s, his mentor was the legendary Beat poet Allen Ginsberg. His books include *To day—Minutes only* (a prose-poem sequence with Saadi Youssef), a poetry/music collaboration *Blue Square, Che: A Novella In Three Parts*, and *American Drone: New & Select Poems*. He is co-translator with Sinan Antoon of Saadi Youssef's poems in *Nostalgia, My Enemy*, also director of Harbor Mountain Press, publishing, among others, writers from Cambodia, Croatia, Cuba, Cyprus, Iraq, Spain and UK.

Hassan Najmi is a Moroccan poet and writer, publishing his work since 1977. Today he is one of Morocco's best known poets with four collections of poems, the novel *Gertrude* (reviewed above) and two books of essays, one with the artist Kacimi. He has been arts editor of *Al-Ittihad al-Ishtiraki* newspaper, President of the Moroccan Union of Writers (1998–2005), and was director-general of the Book and Publications Department of Morocco's Ministry of Culture.

Khalil Suwailih was born in Syria in 1959. He has three poetry collections and four novels. He is cultural editor of the Syrian newspaper *Teshreen*, and a correspondent for *Al-Akhbar* newspaper and Radio Monte Carlo. In 2009 his novel *Warraq al-Hubb* (*Writing Love*, AUC Press, 2012) won the Naguib Mahfouz Medal for Literature.

Cristina Viti is a poet and translator of contemporary Italian poetry and fiction. Her translations include the poetry of Dino Campana (*Selected Works*, Survivors' Press 2006) and Mariapia Veladiano's award-winning first novel *A Life Apart* (MacLehose, 2013).

Stephen Watts is a poet, editor and translator, with cultural roots in the Swiss Italian Alps and Scotland. He has two bilingual English-Italian works and six poetry collections. His own poetry is translated into Italian, Arabic, Czech and Bengali. He is a Banipal consulting editor.

OTHER CONTRIBUTORS

Charis Bredin has a BA, first class Hons, in French and Arabic (Oxford) and an MA (Distinction) in Arabic Literature (SOAS). She worked part-time at Banipal and is pursuing a PhD at SOAS in modern Arabic Literature.

Peter Clark lived in the Middle East for many years working for the British Council. He has translated works by several contemporary Arab writers including Muhammad al-Murr, Ulfat Idilbi and Selim Matar. His latest publications include *Coffeehouse Footnotes* and a book on Istanbul. He is a Banipal contributing editor.

Mohammed Khair-Eddine (1941–1995) is considered one of the most innovative of francophone Moroccan writers of the 20th century, sometimes called the Dylan Thomas of Morocco. Born and raised in Tafraout, southern Morocco, he joined the circle of writers known as the Amitiés littéraires et artistiques in Casablanca and was a co-founder of the Poésie toute movement. He lived in France for many years, and after 1979 between Morocco and France until his death in 1995 on Morocco's Independence Day, November 18. *Banipal 10/11* (2001) has a major feature on his work, with more poems from his *Soleil arachnide* collection.

Norbert Hirschhorn is a poet and doctor specializing in international public health. His poetry is published in three collections, as well as in journals and anthologies. Born in Minnesota, USA, he now lives between London and Beirut.

Ghada Mourad is a PhD candidate in Comparative Literature and a Schaeffer Fellow in Literary Translation at the University of California, Irvine. She translates from Arabic and French into English, and her translations have appeared in many US journals, including *Jadaliyya, Transference, Metamorphoses* and *ArteEast*.

Robin Ostle is an Emeritus Research Fellow at St John's College, University of Oxford, where the principal focus of his current research is on Literature and the Fine Arts in Egypt in the 20th century. He is President of the Academic Council of the Mediterranean Institute of the Humanities and Social Sciences (University of Aix-Marseille). His most recent major publication is *Sensibilities of the Islamic Mediterranean* (I B Tauris, London 2009).

Youssef Rakha was born on 12 June 1976 in Cairo. He has a first class BA Hons in English and Philosophy (Hull University, UK, 1998). He has one collection of short stories (1999) and two travel books, including *Beirut, shi mahal* (Beirut, some place, 2006), and a novel, *The Book of the Sultan's Seal*, excerpted above.

Ghalya Al Said is a poet and writer from Oman, living between London and Muscat. She has a PhD in International Relations from Warwick University. She writes poetry in both English and Arabic, and has published three novels in Arabic, her debut *Ayam fil-Jannah* (Days of Heaven, 2005) excerpted above.

Paul Starkey is Emeritus Professor of Arabic at Durham University, Vice-President of the British Society for Middle Eastern Studies and Chair of the Banipal Trust for Arab Literature. He has translated many works by contemporary Arab authors, the latest being Youssef Rakha's *The Book of the Sultan's Seal*, excerpted above (Interlink, 2014). He is a Banipal contributing editor.

Susannah Tarbush is a freelance journalist specialising in cultural affairs in the Middle East. She writes the Tanjara blog, and is a consulting editor of Banipal and a regular book reviewer.

Aoe Tanami is a Japanese researcher in Middle Eastern Studies, currently serving as a Chief Research Fellow of the Center for Asian Pacific Studies, Seikei University. She is strongly committed to the Palestine issue, following the cultural activities and contemporary literature of Palestine. Her award-winning Japanese book *Absentees' Israel: Culture of Occupation and Palestine* was translated this year into Korean.

Mona Zaki is an Egyptian, born in Belgrade. She has a BA from the American University in Cairo in Middle Eastern History and a PhD on the Medieval Muslim depiction of hell from Princeton University. She is a Banipal contributing editor.

GUEST LITERATURE –
DUTCH AUTHORS AND
TRANSLATORS

Jan-Willem Anker has four collections of poetry and has been a programmer for the Rotterdam Poetry International. His work has been translated into French and German. In 2012 he published the historical novel *Een beschaafde man* (A Civilised Man), excerpted above, based on the life of the notorious British art collector Lord Elgin.

Hanna Bervoets writes novels, columns and scripts. Her columns for *Volkskrant* magazine are hugely popular in the Netherlands. She won the 2009 Debut Novel of the Year Award for her first novel and her second was awarded the Opzij Literature Prize 2012 for best book by a female Dutch author. It has since been adapted for film.

Benjamin Burg is the author of the short story collections *Camera, Leo, de vrouwenman* (Leo, the Ladies Man) and the novel *Redder in nood* (The Life Saver). His work has been published in several literary magazines. He is the founder of the interactive Creative Writing Academy EDITIO and lives in Amsterdam.

David Doherty was born in London and raised in Scotland. After studying English and Literary Linguistics in Glasgow he moved to Amsterdam where he has been a Dutch to English translator for the past 15 years.

Brian Doyle (b. Scotland, 1956) has translated a wide range of academic and literary works from Dutch/Flemish into English in addition to teaching Hebrew at the University of Leuven in Belgium. His recent literary translations include Jacqueline van Maarsen's *Inheriting Anne Frank* (2010) and Tessa de Loo's *The Book of Doubt* (2011). He also translates poetry and literary non-fiction.

Stephan Enter (b. 1968) has a collection of short stories Winterhanden (Chilblained Hands) and three novels, with his first *Lichtjaren* (Light Years, 2004), nominated for the Libris Literature Prize. His second, *Spel* (Game, 2007) was a great success in Germany and his third, *Grip*, excerpted above, was a best-seller with editions in German, Italian and Norwegian forthcoming.

Michele Hutchison (b. UK, 1972) worked as an editor in the publishing industry before turning to translation. She lives in Amsterdam and has translated works by Simone van der Vlugt, Joris Luyendijk, Ilja Leonard Pfeijffer, Tosca Menten, amongst others. She is currently translating the Flemish writer Tom Lanoye.

Franca Treur won the 2010 Selexyz Debut Prize for her bestselling novel *Dorsvloer vol confetti* (Confetti on the Threshing Floor), excerpted above, which will be released as a feature-length film this autumn. Her second novel is *De woongroep* (The Roommates, 2014). She contributes stories, columns and essays to *NRC Handelsblad, Volkskrant, Groene Amsterdammer*, Radio I VPRO Nooit meer slapen and *Vogue*.

Victor Schiferli (b. 1967, the Netherlands) is a writer and poet, and international advisor for fiction at the Dutch Foundation for Literature (www.letterenfonds.nl), supporting the translation of books from the Netherlands. He has three poetry collections and one novel *Dromen van Schalkwijk* (Dreams of Schalkwijk, 2012). Schiferli has edited several anthologies and has also worked as a journalist, critic and photographer.

Hester Velmans is a translator specializing in contemporary Dutch and French literature. Her translation of Renate Dorrestein's *A Heart of Stone* won the Vondel Prize in 2001; in early 2014 she was awarded a US National Endowment of the Arts Fellowship to translate the neglected novelist Herman Franke.

Laura Watkinson lives in Amsterdam and translates from Dutch, German and Italian. Her recent translations include Tonke Dragt's *The Letter for the King* (Pushkin) and Cees Nooteboom's *Letters to Poseidon* (MacLehose Press).

Robbert Welagen (b. 1981) made his debut at the age of twenty-five with the novella *Lipari* (Selexyz Debut Prize 2007). Since then he has published four more novels, with his fifth *The Disappearance of Robbert*, excerpted above, nominated for the prestigious Libris Prize.

For more information on all the authors in *Banipal 51* and all the translators, writers, book reviewers and artists, please go to:

www.banipal.co.uk/contributors/

To SUBSCRIBE TO PRINT BANIPAL see page 185 or go to: http://www.banipal.co.uk/subscribe/
To SUBSCRIBE TO DIGITAL BANIPAL or make a trial, see page 82 or go to:
http://www.exacteditions.com/browse/20700/21379